"Oh, Lindsey . . . you've brought love into my life. Whatever happens, that was worth it all!"

From that moment the dreariness of the past weeks evaporated as though it had never been. She felt Trey's arms slip beneath her as she was carried to the bedroom; her clothes dropped in a crumpled pile on the floor, his robe joining them seconds later.

Lindsey had dreamed many times of how it would be making love with Trey. In those vivid, erotic fantasies they coaxed every nuance of sensual pleasure from each other with exquisite slowness. But now it was explosive and desperate—no control was possible. . . .

A Matter of Trust

REBECCA FLANDERS

A Love Affair from
HARLEQUIN
London · Toronto · New York · Sydney

First published in Great Britain in 1984
by Harlequin, 15–16 Brook's Mews, London W1A 1DR

© Rebecca Flanders 1983

ISBN 0 263 74631 3

18/0284

Made and printed in Great Britain by
Cox & Wyman Ltd, Reading

Chapter One

During business hours the building was the center of frenetic activity, the very pulse-beat of the downtown legal community. But at eight o'clock at night it was deserted. The overhead fluorescents gave off a sleepy, otherworldly aura, and Lindsey Madison's footsteps echoed with a noisy clatter on the tiled floor as she hurried to the elevator. And then, rounding the corner at a breakneck pace, she drew herself up sharply to avoid a collision with someone who reached the corner just as she did, coming from the opposite direction. Her slick-soled sandals skidded on the waxed floor and she lost her balance, throwing her arm out to catch herself and berating herself impatiently; *Clumsy, clumsy...*

The man caught her arm in a firm and automatic grip, and she flashed him an apologetic smile as she quickly righted herself and said breathlessly, "Sorry!" He nodded to her impersonally and released her arm, and she felt a quick stain of color touch her cheeks as, for just a split second, her eyes were captured by a pair of the softest, most beautiful cocoa-velvet eyes she had ever seen. She was embarrassed by her clumsiness and startled at finding another person in the empty building and taken aback by the near collision—surely her quick, almost schoolgirlish blush was due to no more than that. She wasn't expecting to encounter anyone on this floor, much less a young man with tousled chestnut hair and soulful dark eyes, and for just the briefest moment she allowed herself to be distracted from the urgency of her destination, wondering who he was and what he was doing here this time of night; but it was really hardly longer than the space of a breath before she gave him another quick, polite smile, and hurried away, intent upon reaching the fifth floor with all possible speed.

She was almost an hour late, which wasn't unusual for her, but she justified to herself that it really wasn't her fault. She had read that Atlanta traffic was the third worst in the world—outranked only by that in Paris and Los Angeles—and her first independent excursion into the downtown area had resulted in her becoming lost no less than three times, finally ending up back on the freeway going in the opposite direction from where she wanted to be. And although she had never driven in either Paris or Los Angeles, she was ready to concede first prize for worst traffic to Atlanta, and assured herself that even if she hadn't gotten lost—and even if she *had* allowed herself extra time, which she had fully intended to do in the first place—she still would have been late. To make matters worse, it had started to rain and her car was acting funny, threatening to stall each time she slowed down or braked. She hoped Art maintained his usual good humor when she explained the situation, and she hoped he was not as hungry as she was.

It wasn't until she reached the elevator that she noticed the gentleman she had almost bumped into was still with her. His hand reached the elevator button first and she let her own hand drop, stealing a quick glance at him which was laced with remembered embarrassment and, strangely, a small bit of pleasure that she would not be making this elevator ride alone. The glance was too brief for her to notice much about him other than the fact that he was not as young as she had first thought—in his mid-thirties, perhaps—and he was wearing a gray sweatsuit and jogging shoes, which was, she had to admit, not the type of attire one usually expected to see in this building, even after hours. Then the elevator doors swung open in almost immediate response to his touch, and he stepped inside. Lindsey hurried in after him, pushing the button for the fifth floor.

For a moment he hesitated, and she could feel his eyes on her. She glanced at him with another little smile, just long enough to catch a glimpse of something confusingly like impatient disapproval in the cynical tightening of his dark brows, and then she looked away, pulling the collar of her white rabbit jacket up around her neck in annoyance. She could not imagine what she had done to deserve such a look; after all, it was not as though she had actually knocked him down in the near-collision, and it had not even been her fault! The elevator lurched into motion, and he reached in front of her to press number seven, then deliberately walked to the other side of the car, as though he found her very presence distasteful. With an imperceptible shrug of her shoulders, she dismissed his apparent bad humor and fretted anxiously for the elevator to reach its destination.

That happened sooner than she expected, and the wrenching stop of the elevator caught her off balance, almost resulting in another display of her clumsiness. But she steadied herself quickly against the wall, not glancing at the other occupant of the cubicle, and stepped forth expectantly to the door, already forming her apology speech to Art in her head. She glanced at her watch and stifled a groan. She only hoped Art had waited for her. And the door did not open.

Impatiently, she reached for the button marked "open" and a smooth voice drawled behind her, "I wouldn't, if I were you."

She turned, surprise registering on her face. So, he could talk! But rather than explaining further, he simply nodded to the area over the door. She stepped back in puzzlement to follow the direction of his gaze, and then she gasped out loud in impatience and alarm. The little light had stopped halfway between three and four. They were stuck!

In desperation, she jabbed at the button marked five a couple of times, and then stepped back expectantly, watching the register above the door. Nothing. She let out a long, soft groan of despair, accompanied by a barely audible, "*Oh, damn*!" Almost an hour late and stuck in the elevator. Art would never forgive her this time, and this was definitely not the way to impress the other members of the committee, nor to assure her uncle that his faith in her was well placed. She groaned again and leaned back against the wall, closing her eyes briefly. *What a mess!*

The man stepped in front of her and pushed the emergency button. Very far away, she thought she could hear the drone of a bell. "It's happened before," he assured her, but there was little sympathy in his tone or eyes. "Someone will get it started again, though it may take a few minutes."

She looked at him with sudden hope. "How long?" she insisted.

He shrugged. "We'll have to wait until the security guard makes his rounds and hears the alarm, then he'll have to go to the basement and flip a switch. It may be a while."

Her shoulders sagged and she released another little breath of despair. In other words, it could be hours. What a thing to happen, just when she was trying to make an impression. She looked at her companion in hopes of distracting herself from her own misery and explained, "I'm late for an appointment."

The twist of his brow was sardonic and there was a tone in his voice she did not quite like as he replied, "This time of night?"

The way he said that implied disbelief, and his look subtly accused her of breaking and entering, at the least. She felt compelled to explain, though somewhat stiffly, "A dinner date, actually. I didn't want to be late."

He looked at her as though wondering what she expected him to do about it, then walked deliberately back to his own side of the elevator. As he was now standing directly opposite her, it was impossible not to look at him, and Lindsey was too new to big-city life to have developed the art of secluding herself in a crowd by staring straight at people without seeing them. He, however, had apparently had a great deal of practice. He chose a point just above her right shoulder to stare at and never once removed his gaze. *And,* she reflected wryly, *I always thought of Atlanta as a very friendly city!* Well, she decided with an inner shrug, if he could be rude, so could she, and she stared unabashedly.

His behavior in no way matched his appearance. In the casual running suit and with that slightly rumpled chestnut hair he looked slightly boyish, despite his height and mature frame. He was leanly built, the trimness of his waist and the hardness of his thighs notable despite the bulky suit; she thought he must run a lot. His face could not be described as handsome—not in the usual devastating way one might describe a Robert Redford for example—but it was attractive. There was a firmness about his features which suggested a man of authority, hinting at an unbending nature in the set of his jaw and the squareness of his chin. But if there was hardness in his face, Lindsey easily ignored that less than desirable attribute because of the signs of gentleness she found elsewhere—most especially about the eyes. The eyebrows fascinated her. She had read about "the poetic sweep of his brow" and "brows delicately arched like wings," but she had never seen anyone who could actually fit that description. It seemed almost sinful that such beauty should belong to a man. His eyebrows were thick and a perfect brown, and they really did arch over the bone in poetic symmetry, shadowing eyes that were just as rich and brown, and just as beautiful. His lashes, too, were as thick and lovely as a woman's, and the entire effect was one of gentleness, perception, and compassion. Without those eyes his would have been a very ordinary face; with them it was arresting and even attractive, and Lindsey made an immediate judgment of his character on the basis of his eyes alone. He was probably a very nice man, tender and capable of great emotion, and why he looked at this moment as though his face would crack if he smiled was beyond her.

She wondered once again who he was and what he was doing in this building after hours in such unlikely attire. This man, she thought idly, might be a high school coach—track, not football; he had the honest, upright, yet youthful appearance that would make him perfect for the job. But no, the eyes, the fluffy shock of unruly brown hair—he would be a writer. Science fiction or fantasy. He had the definite look of a dreamer about him. Upon closer scrutiny of the set of his mouth, the faintly noticeable grooves etched on either side, she decided there was something a bit more serious about him than would be apparent in the average fantasy writer's face, and she found a suitable category for him: He was a scholar, of course, of the fine arts or perhaps even dead languages, maybe archaeology—

something that required great intellectual ability but was of very little practical use. So what was he doing here?

She had thought him to be completely oblivious to her scrutiny, but as he turned coolly assessing eyes on her, she realized that he was perfectly aware she had been staring and was completely indifferent to the fact. She felt an annoying blush sting her cheeks again and she shifted her eyes quickly to the indicator light above the door. "My goodness!" she exclaimed, a little more loudly than she had intended. "What's taking so long?"

But rather than answering, he simply commented, flickering his gaze over her diminutive figure once without much show of interest, "I know everyone in this building, but I don't recall seeing you before."

She picked up his lead, glad for the opportunity to break the uncomfortable silence. "I've never been here before," she explained. "It just seemed easier to meet here since we were supposed to get some business done before dinner."

She would have clarified further, but his definite lack of interest stopped her. He nodded once and made no further effort to continue the conversation. In the small confines of the elevator, enforced silence was annoying, and Lindsey tried to draw him out.

"Do you work here?" she suggested, hardly believing it. The last thing she would have guessed him to be was a lawyer, and she was rather disappointed.

He gave only a noncommittal "Hmm" and leaned back against the wall, crossing his arms, and his long legs at the ankles, looking at the door.

She made a face which he could not see and turned her own gaze to the door. This was really stupid. Two grownup people at the mercy of modern technology, reduced to staring at a mechanical door with all the

helpless expectancy of children waiting for a rabbit to
pop out of a hat. *That's the last time,* she decided grimly,
*I put any stock in first impressions. He had looked like such
a friendly person.*

She sighed again softly and shifted restlessly against
the wall, thrusting her hands into the pockets of her
furry jacket. She suddenly felt very conspicuous dressed
as she was in comparison to his casual garb, and now it
appeared to be his turn to stare She could feel h is eyes
upon her but did not return his gaze.

The plans had been for dinner at the Plaza and
drinks afterward at one of the nicer nightclubs, and
Lindsey had dressed accordingly. Not forgetting that
the main purpose of the evening had been a sort of
get-acquainted business dinner, she had dressed simply though elegantly in a clinging plum-colored skirt
and white satin blouse. Her stockings were a very pale
shade of plum with just a hint of metallic silver here
and there, and her black sandals had three-and-a-half
inch heels. She had worn the jacket because, in early
April, the nights were still chilly, and because she knew
it was one of her most complimentary garments. The
white fur was the perfect frame for her rose-and-cream
complexion (a pale sprinkling of freckles hidden as well
as possible by makeup), and its texture added new di-
mensions of richness to her dark auburn hair. She had
been told that her hair was her most striking feature,
and was often asked why she did not wear it longer.
The answer was simply that she hadn't the time or the
patience to dress herself up like a model every morning, and long hair seemed to her more trouble than it
was worth. In consequence, it was styled casually, tailored just above the collar in the back and over her
ears, but thick and luxuriant on top and over her forehead. The short cut brought out highlights of deep gold
and warm, rich reds, which were in places almost dark

enough to be called mahogany; the effect was a stunning combination of deep colors in a slightly tousled, little-care hairstyle that suited her personality perfectly.

She forcefully restrained herself from responding to his scrutiny; obviously he was paying her back for having subjected him to the same sort of examination only moments ago. She tried to ignore him. The minutes wore on and on against the faint background humming of the faraway bell. She wondered if anyone would ever hear it. The security guard could be on his dinner break, for goodness' sake, or he could decide to skip rounds tonight or he could be on a long telephone call with his girlfriend.... *Damn!* she thought again angrily, but she knew there was no point in voicing her frustration to her companion. He couldn't care less.

A male voice broke through her rather distracted thoughts. "You're not from around here, are you?"

She turned to him in surprise, and her irritation with the entire situation, combined with hunger and an increasing nervousness, caused her to say exactly what was on her mind. "So! You do have more than one sentence in your repertoire! I suppose," she added, grateful to hear even the sound of her own voice breaking the silence, "since we appear to be fated to spend the night together, you've decided talking is better than nothing."

He lifted one eyebrow cryptically, but she caught the beginning of a twinkle in the depths of his warm brown eyes. "Most women," he pointed out, "don't appreciate advances from strange men."

And again, because she was so grateful to have someone to talk to, she said the first thing that came to mind. "Oh? Are you making advances?"

He replied evenly, though the beginnings of a smile tugged intriguingly at the corners of his lips, "Since, if I'm not mistaken, you've just invited me to spend the

A Matter of Trust

night with you, I suppose an advance or two wouldn't be out of place."

She drew her brows together, fighting back a blush of confusion, and almost wished she hadn't encouraged him. Then, to her very great surprise, he slid down against the wall, sitting on the carpeted floor and looping his arms negligently about his upraised knees. He patted the place on the floor beside him. "Make yourself comfortable," he invited. "Looks like we're going to be here awhile."

She tried to look forbidding and remained standing. In a moment, he had transformed himself from the stern, distant, almost hostile companion in misfortune to the relaxed, friendly person she had imagined him to be in the first place... but the transformation made her slightly uneasy. She knew that men—especially those of short acquaintance—often mistook her friendly, open manner for something else, and more than once she had found herself on the receiving end of attentions she had not meant to encourage. She knew this was a personality trait she should try to curb, but Lindsey very rarely remembered to be cautious until it was too late.

He said, just as though he were picking up a thread of conversation which had never been interrupted, "But then again, most women would never have gotten on an elevator in a deserted building with a strange man in the first place."

She was aware of his speculative, almost probing gaze, and that only served to confuse her more. "What in the world are you talking about?" she demanded, momentarily distracted from her brooding thoughts about her missed dinner and her missed appointment. "I had to get to the fifth floor somehow! What did you expect me to do—fly?"

He laughed softly, resting his chin on his double fists

while his eyes appraised her with frank mirth. "Okay, it's driving me crazy. Where *are* you from?"

She noted the change of subject with some irritation, and replied in a slightly disgruntled tone, "What makes you think I wasn't born right here in Atlanta?"

"Your accent, for one thing," he replied easily, and she bristled.

"I do not have an accent!" she insisted hotly, for the teasing she had endured during the first semester of college had caused her to undertake a program of self-improvement designed to wipe away all vocal traces of her Southern background.

"Oh, yes you do," he contradicted mildly. Just barely—more of a drawl, really, but very deep South. Most Atlantans, surprisingly enough, have no accent at all. I would say yours is from"—he glanced at her thoughtfully—"Alabama? Louisiana?"

"New Orleans," she supplied grudgingly, and he looked pleased.

"Ah, yes," he murmured, "the bayou country. Some of the most beautiful dialect in the world is used there, if it's spoken properly. But you haven't lived there for a while; you've got a Yankee twang."

She was totally unaware of being led into revealing her life story. "I just moved here from Iowa," she explained. "I've lived there for eight years."

He nodded. "That explains it, then. Small town, right?"

"Not all that small," she defended. "A university town. That explains what?"

"Your obvious lack of street-wisdom," he replied. "Why you didn't wait for another elevator like a smart girl should have, and why, by the way, you now find yourself trapped between floors with a man who could be Jack the Ripper for all you know."

The reminder of her predicament served to exasperate her all over again, and she exclaimed impatiently, "The elevator again! Are you blaming *me* because it broke down? What's the big deal, anyway?"

He looked up blandly. "Look at yourself. Look at the danger you could be in. What if I had stopped the elevator on purpose? It wouldn't have been hard to do, you know, and as you've already seen, the emergency bell is next to useless this time of night. I could be armed. I could be a thief, a rapist, or a psychopath. And here you are... helpless."

Although she could not deny feeling helpless, she was certainly no more helpless than he was in the present situation, and the very idea that he could be any of those horrible things he had just suggested was patently absurd. She cocked her head to the side and tried to smother a smile as she demanded, "Well, which are you? A thief, a psychopath, or a rapist?"

He looked at her for a moment in slow amusement mingled with amazement, and simply shook his head in gentle exasperation. "It's incredible," he murmured, mostly to himself. "Millions of tax dollars spent on educating the public to crime awareness and this"—he gestured vaguely in her direction without looking up—"is the result. You have fantastic legs, by the way."

Realizing that his position on the floor gave him a good view of her legs and little else made her somewhat uncomfortable, and she suspected that was exactly what he had been trying to do with this entire conversation—make her uncomfortable. She refused to be intimidated, however, and she crossed her ankles casually, arching her foot against the wall to give him a better view, and replied nonchalantly to his compliment, "Thanks. Yours aren't bad, either."

He looked up at her, humor now bubbling madly in his eyes, and suggested, "Shall I turn off the emergency alarm?"

She struggled to hide a smile. She was more aware of him now than she would have liked to have been, but it was a singularly pleasant sensation...and rather disturbing. At the same moment that she felt as though she had made a friend, she wondered whether once again she had gotten herself into a situation she was not equipped to deal with. She did not let any of that show on her face, though, as she removed her eyes from the study of his strong brown wrists looped about his knees and the intriguing outline of muscles through the unattractive fabric of his sweatsuit, and she tried to put the memory of those poetic brows out of her mind as she turned her eyes to the ceiling. "A real hero-type," she mused, after a moment, "would find a way to climb out that trapdoor and rescue me."

"Fortunately, heroism is not one of my virtues," he replied, and in a moment followed her gaze to the ceiling. "Is there really a trapdoor up there? I always thought that stuff was just for Hollywood."

She thought she could make out the outline of a panel in the ceiling, and she became cautiously excited. "I think it is," she said, and looked at him hopefully. "Do you think...?"

He got up and stood beside her, craning his neck to examine the ceiling. She was very aware of his nearness, the contained strength in his sinewy body, the faint scent of masculinity and perspiration. She kept her eyes on the ceiling.

"Well, I'll be damned," he murmured after a moment. "It really is a trapdoor." And he went back and sat on the floor again.

She tried not to look too crestfallen. It was just that she was really beginning to fear they might be stuck here until morning, and Art would never believe this story, and she was starving.

By now she had all but given up hope that Art would

have waited for her. She had unfortunately acquired a reputation for unpredictability and unreliability over the years, which Art as well as her Uncle Addison knew only too well. She had no doubt she would be forgiven eventually, but she had so wanted to make a good impression in this new city with a new job, and she could just see Art and Uncle Addison now, chatting over dinner with their colleagues about "the same old Lindsey— she hasn't changed a bit," laughing and relating anecdotes from the past. The image grated, and she wasn't sure whether it was from embarrassment or because the very thought of dinner reminded her again that she was starving.

Lindsey was a professor of political science, which always came as a surprise to anyone who was introduced to the petite, red-haired girl who, unless she made a concentrated effort to appear otherwise, generally did not look old enough to be out of high school. She was, in fact, twenty-nine years old, had just completed her doctorate, and had been with the same midwestern university for almost five years. She had distinguished herself with local political work, and her experience with the party on a national level during the presidential elections had given her the confidence she needed to finally go after her ultimate goal—a position in Washington. She knew it was for her professional abilities, rather than her personal attributes, that Uncle Addison had offered her a paid position on his re-election committee, with the promise of that much-coveted Washington job when he won—which Lindsey had no doubt he would. Addison Cantrell had already served two terms in the U.S. Senate, his constituency was large and loyal, and his competition, in Lindsey's opinion, posed very little threat. She had not thought twice about leaving her home, her friends, her job, and the possibility of tenure at the university. This was what she wanted, and the time was right to do the job she was best at, to live the life she loved.

For Lindsey was good at her job. Behind her desk she was efficient, organized, decisive, and given to flashes of brilliance. She could command a lecture hall filled with students or a campaign headquarters in the last moments of pre-election crisis with an unruffled calm and an authoritative ease which drew attention to her like metal shavings to a magnet and left no doubt in anyone's mind as to who was boss. She was never at a loss for inspiration, she never panicked during a crisis. But once she left her office, a strange transformation overtook her. She could get lost on her way home from the supermarket, her social life was a wreck because she had never been on time in her life, and no one trusted her to take papers out of the office because, somehow, magically, they always disappeared before she reached her apartment. She forgot to return phone calls and rarely cooked for herself because of an unfortunate tendency to leave the oven on and not notice the smoke—a habit which had caused neighbors to alarm the fire department unnecessarily on more than one occasion. Art called her "the original absent-minded professor," and Lindsey had learned to ignore his teasing over the years. It was only that, on this occasion, she had wanted to make an effort to appear as efficient and organized outside the office as she was inside, but with a sigh, she resigned herself to the fact that that was not to be her fate. Art would just have to understand one more time.

Her companion said suddenly, "Those shoes must be killing you. Why don't you take them off?"

As a matter of fact, her feet were more accustomed to moccasins and practical two-inch heels than the fashionable torture-chamber devices she now wore, but she knew better than to remove her shoes in a public place. She always forgot them when she left. Instead, after a moment, she followed his example and sank to the floor, slanting her legs sideways and pulling the hem of her skirt down as far as it would go. And although she had not meant to, after arranging her limbs and her clothing for both decency and comfort, she found they were sitting almost shoulder to shoulder. He smiled. "That's better."

"Is it?" she responded morosely, staring straight ahead at the immovable door. Looking at it only made her hungrier, and her thoughts were filled with despair — not only at having to miss her dinner and spend the night on a cold, hard floor, but at having to explain it all to Art in the morning and knowing he would be laughing about it for the rest of her natural life.

"Well" — lightly, his fingers rested on the sensuous softness of her fur-covered arm — "I could think of worse ways to spend an evening...."

Lindsey was really in no mood for this, and as she turned to make some flip retort she was startled to find his face much closer to hers than she had expected. For a brief moment she seemed to be totally lost in those warm brown eyes and she forgot what she had been about to say. She was very aware of the gentle touch of his strong, lean fingers on her arm, and of a change taking place within her which she suspected, perhaps falsely, was overcoming him as well. It was ridiculous, two strangers in a stalled elevator gazing into one another's eyes in one of those much-lauded and greatly romanticized magical moments of discovery.... She couldn't believe she was actually playing out such a clichéd scene, and later she would laugh nervously at herself for allowing her imagination to run wild, but in that moment there was no doubt about it. What flowed between them, so tangibly she could almost see it, what caused a quivering of her insides and a peculiar warm flush to spread over her body, was a very definite and unmistakable sexual chemistry, a type she had never experienced before and had never imagined existed outside the pages of books. It hit her so suddenly, with no warning and no prelude other than the power of his light touch and his overwhelming nearness, that there was no time to raise defenses. Her pulses accelerated wildly as he moved his face just a fraction closer to hers and all she could see was those deep brown eyes; a warmth from his body seemed to engulf her, and she knew it was crazy, but he was going to kiss her. And she was going to let him.

And then, abruptly, he stiffened. As though a door had been forcibly slammed shut, the light was extinguished from his eyes, leaving them cold and remote again. The mask of his face tightened into a grimness; lines of anger appeared at the corners of his lips, and all she felt from him now was an unmistakable hostility. He straightened up abruptly, and the expression on his face was thinly disguised loathing. In the space of a heartbeat he had metamorphosed from a living being into a statue, and she recoiled as though struck, rampaging confusion and hot embarrassment sweeping through her.

But she hardly had the space of a breath to sort out the tangled emotions and events of the past few seconds, for without further preamble the elevator lurched into motion. She scrambled to her feet, feeling him rise more stiffly behind her, and she went to stand urgently at the door. When it opened, she hurried through without a backward glance.

Chapter Two

She heard the elevator door close softly behind her as she made her way toward Art's office, her steps rapid on the carpeted floor, her color high. She could not believe she had almost let herself be kissed by a strange man on an elevator; she could not believe that she had acted like a moonstruck teenager; she could not believe that even now her heart was pounding and her composure was in shreds.

Such things usually did not happen to her. It was true that every other bizarre, unusual, and incredible circumstance usually managed to seek her out sooner or later, accounting for her harum-scarum life-style and her string of unbelievable tales and excuses to friends and relatives—but brief, poignant, romantic encounters were not usually among them. Her last meaningful relationship with a man had been over a year ago, when both parties concerned had realized they were better friends than lovers. Neither one had been exactly heartbroken when he had been transferred out of the state, and they still corresponded sporadically. Such was the story of her life, and she really could not believe she had acted so silly with a perfect stranger.

She reached the frosted glass door which was marked

Arthur J. Madison, Attorney at Law, and as she had expected, a white legal envelope with her name scrawled across it was taped to the frame.

She squared her shoulders and with a sigh put the events of the past few moments behind her as she opened the envelope and read the note inside. "Lin— Given your record, I'm sure you'll understand why we didn't wait. I'll call you later—Art." And across the bottom of the page: "P.S. This one had better be good."

She sighed again and folded the note into her purse. For a moment she debated whether to answer his note in equally caustic terms, but decided it might be best not to antagonize him. She would call him and explain later tonight or early in the morning, before he left for the office. She thought he might have at least mentioned where they were going after dinner, and for another moment she considered trying to catch up with them at the Plaza. But no, the way her luck was running tonight such an attempt could only lead to catastrophe. She started slowly back toward the elevator.

For a moment longer she hesitated with her hand near the button, then she made one of the few prudent decisions of her life. She took the stairs.

Her clattering footsteps echoed and re-echoed down the stairwell for five floors, and when she finally pushed open the heavy door to the lobby she was flushed and a little breathless with exertion. Her rather flustered appearance was not changed by the sight of a tall, familiar figure moving toward her, a legal-sized manila folder tucked casually beneath his arm, one beautiful brow raised in sardonic amusement.

"Once burned, twice wary, hmm?" he commented, and for a moment she was too confused by his unexpected appearance to respond.

Then she laughed nervously and brushed at the thick fall of hair across her forehead. "Oh, you mean the stairs!" She glanced back at them as she started toward the exit. "Well, no sense in taking any more chances tonight, I guess." She was surprised when he fell into place beside her, and she ventured a brief glance at him, trying to forget what had happened—or what she had imagined had happened—between them in the elevator. "I—didn't expect to see you again."

"Naturally, I waited for you."

A leap of pleasure caught in her throat and must have shown in her eyes, because he explained with another sardonic quirk of his eyebrow, "I thought you might need someone to walk you to your car."

It was the way it was said, not the words themselves, which disappointed Lindsey. It was, in fact, very thoughtful of him and unexpectedly polite, but he made it seem so much like a necessary courtesy or even an annoying duty that much of the charm of the gesture was lost. Lindsey found herself quickening her steps as she tossed a bright smile over her shoulder to hide what was, after all, a very silly reaction to a polite offer. "No thanks," she replied. "There's really no need. I'm parked in the garage here."

He lengthened his stride effortlessly and reached the door before her, placing his fingers lightly on her elbow as he escorted her through. She had the feeling he wanted to make some comment about the dangers of a dimly lit parking garage for a woman alone but was forcefully restraining himself. She was vaguely irritated with him.

As they stepped into the misty concrete parking area he commented, "Stood up, huh?"

She grimaced. "Well, I can't really blame him. I was only an hour and a half late."

He inquired with absolutely no change of expression, "Husband or boyfriend?"

"Worse," she answered dully, not looking at him. "Brother."

She hesitated, scanning the nearly empty parking level for her car. The pillars and twisting lanes resembled a maze to her, and she could not immediately remember where, exactly, she had parked. "Oh," she said with relief, spotting her rather weathered-looking white Maverick in a corner, "there it is."

He walked with her across the concrete floor and even opened the door for her. She slid behind the wheel and found her keys, glad only to be in a familiar place with the night almost over. She smiled up at him, but could think of nothing to say other than, "Thanks."

He responded with, "Good night," and closed her door. She watched him leave, fighting back a strange and rather piquant reflection that all the interesting people she met seemed to flit in and out of her life without her ever having a chance to know them, and it was too bad that this time could not be different. Then she inserted her key into the ignition switch and turned the starter.

The motor did not catch immediately, but that was not unusual. She pumped the accelerator and tried again. And again. The engine ground purposefully but gave no indication of catching. She refused to believe this was happening. She pumped the accelerator with more vigor and twisted the key. This time she was rewarded with a sporadic coughing and shuddering of the motor, but again it died without further signs of life. She should have accepted defeat, but even as she was wondering in despair and frustration what to do next, she continued trying to coax her worn-out little car into life.

She couldn't believe her bad luck. Who to call, what to do? The only two people she knew in Atlanta were presently having dinner together, laughing about her, and they would be no help at all. She supposed she could go down and ask the parking attendant for the name of a nearby service station and then use one of the pay phones inside. She wasn't even sure she had a quarter. She hoped she had her credit card. She gave up her futile efforts to start the car, then checked her purse, in the process overturning a litter basket hanging from the dashboard. Out spilled almost six months' worth of soiled tissues, crumpled candy wrappers, grocery lists, receipts, and squashed paper cups. She uttered a small oath and ignored the mess all over the floor of her car as she rummaged through her purse. Credit cards were there, but she remembered too late she hadn't had time to go to the bank that day and her wallet was empty. A thorough search of her change purse produced two pennies, a button, and a lint-covered breath mint. She didn't even have cab fare home.

For a moment she sat there, her arms looped across the steering wheel, staring bleakly at the gray wall in front of her. Being trapped in an elevator was one thing, but if there was any feeling more helpless or frustrating than being stranded in a car that wouldn't start, Lindsey did not know what it was. And then, determinedly, she squared her shoulders and tried it again. She was about due for a change of luck, and it was better than sitting in the empty parking garage trying not to cry.

She did not even notice the car whip into place beside her until the door opened and he got out. When she looked up to see a familiar face and gentle brown eyes now slightly amused as they took in her situation, relief and gratitude swept over her and left her weak.

"Having trouble?" he inquired, coming over to her window.

She nodded, suddenly feeling as though everything was going to be all right—even though the patient mockery in his eyes would have incensed her on any other occasion. "It won't start," she told him, unnecessarily.

He leaned on the open window and suggested, "Have you got gas?"

In panic, her eyes flew to the gauge and to her relief saw it register a quarter of a tank. At least no one could say *this* was her fault. "Yes," she answered. "It's not the battery, either. It just won't catch."

He walked around to the front of the car and opened the hood. Lindsey sank back against the upholstery, reflecting on how strange it was that the sight of a man beneath the hood of a car could forecast sunny skies ahead, promising everything would soon be right with the world.

In a moment, without stepping around, he reported, "You've flooded it, for one thing. I can smell the gas."

She responded with a weak, "Oh," and was glad he could not see her chagrin.

Then he came around to the window again. "But the real problem is that the ignition wires are wet. There's probably condensation in the distributor, too. Do you have a cloth or something?"

Obligingly, she scrambled through the litter on the floor and came up with a handful of lipstick-stained tissues and two paper napkins. He accepted her offering with a looked of amused tolerance. "I really appreciate this," she began, but he had already returned to the front of the car.

He tinkered under the hood for a few minutes, and asked her to try the starter, but she still had no luck.

The process was repeated two or three times, but the stubborn automobile refused to cooperate despite their best efforts. It was with a sinking heart that she saw him close the hood of the car.

She got out to meet him as he explained, ''I don't think there's much we can do tonight; it's still too wet, and you're only running down your battery. You can give it another try in the morning, but I don't like the looks of that distributor cap, and your wires are about shot.'' He gave her a slightly derisive glance. ''You don't do much in the way of maintenance, do you?''

''No,'' she sighed. ''I guess not.'' But she tried not to let her disappointment show as she turned to him with a smile. ''Well, thanks for trying anyway, Mr. —'' She paused inquiringly.

''Trey,'' he supplied, scrubbing his hands on the balled-up napkins. ''All right if I put these back where you found them?''

''Oh . . . yes,'' she answered vaguely, and she missed his humorous glance as he tossed the trash back onto the floor of her car. She glanced at her watch and wondered if by any stretch of the imagination Art could be home now. If not, she would simply have to wait until he was, because someone would have to come and get her. At least, she thought, she could wait in the building, out of the damp air. What a night.

But she managed another smile for her would-be rescuer and repeated, ''I really appreciate all you've done Mr. Trey—''

''No,'' he corrected. ''It's just Trey.'' He opened her car door and stretched inside to press the lock on the passenger side, explaining, ''It's a nickname I got stuck with as a kid—it means third. You know, my grandfather is senior, my father's junior, and I'm Trey. No one ever calls me anything else.''

"Oh," she responded, warming to the fact that he seemed much less remote than on the occasion of their last meeting. He locked the driver's door and slammed it, then turned to her. She smiled and told him, "I'm Lindsey."

He simply lifted an eyebrow quizzically, as though her name was totally irrelevant to the matter at hand — which, of course, it was. She avoided his gaze quickly, embarrassed again, and her eyes fell upon the locked car. She was startled out of her awkwardness.

"What did you do that for?" she questioned. She had fully intended to try to start it again after he left; he surely didn't expect her to just give up and leave it . . . not without a fight, at least. And anyway where did he expect her to go?

"It may not be much of a car," he replied, touching her arm lightly to lead her toward his car in the next space, "but unless you have a spare one hidden away somewhere, I really don't think you want to lose it. Lock your car whenever you leave it."

"But," she protested, "I'm not leaving it. I—"

Again she saw the mocking twist of his eyebrow as he opened the door of his car for her. "You were planning, perhaps, to sit by its side and nurse it through the night? I really don't think that will help. Get in; I'll drive you home."

She hesitated, overwhelmed with relief, but compelled to explain, "But—I live way out of town."

"So do I."

He reached in front of her to remove the manila envelope from the passenger seat and then waited patiently for her to enter. The opportunity was really too heaven-sent to refuse. "Well," she demurred in a moment, "if you're sure it's no trouble . . ."

He waited until she was safely inside to reply, somewhat dryly, "Of course it's trouble. But we won't let that stand in the way of the famous southern hospitality."

She was stung by the remark, and when he got behind the wheel she informed him stiffly, "I insist on paying for your gas and your time. I wouldn't impose except that I don't know anyone in town except my brother and my uncle, and I can't reach them, and I don't have any cash for a cab...." She looked at him, suddenly struck by an idea, and inquired hopefully, "Will you take a check? I won't be able to get to the bank until tomorrow—"

He burst into laughter as the engine roared to life, and she was so startled by this response that she found herself smiling with him. "Lady," he declared, swinging the car out of the parking space, "I think you're a little crazy." And then he turned those twinkling brown eyes on her and added, "Where to?"

She felt herself go warm all over as she told him, "Sandy Springs."

"Well, that's on my way home," he said, "so I can't charge you for the gas." He glanced at her, and in the dim light she could not tell whether or not he was serious. "We'll negotiate the price of my time later."

Always quick on the uptake, she murmured, "That positively reeks of a proposition."

"Since we've already decided to spend the night together," he replied, pulling up to the attendant's window, "I think a proposition would be redundant."

She slanted him a glance, but held her tongue. It promised to be a lively ride home.

He paid the attendant and swung out into the street, switching on the windshield wipers against a slight mist of rain which still clung to the air. The traffic was much lighter than it had been when she arrived, and the streets were dark and shimmery, reflecting headlights and neon signs and the towering lights of hotels and public buildings they passed. He drove with a relaxed ease, one hand on the steering wheel, leaning back against the seat, maneuvering his small car gracefully in and out of the lanes of traffic with an intuitive grace. He wasted no time with scenic tours, but made straight for the expressway, and once caught up in the flow of one-way traffic, he glanced at her and commented, "You've done it again, you know."

She was beginning to relax with the smooth motion of the car and the hypnotic swish of the windshield wipers, and the sound of his voice startled her. She looked at him. "Done what?"

"Only this time," he continued, ignoring her question, "instead of getting into an elevator with a potential psychopath, you've actually gotten into his car and are about to lead him to your home. Not smart, my dear. Not smart at all."

She scowled at him in subdued frustration. She was tired and hungry and discouraged, and she was getting a little bored with the entire line of conversation. "Well," she told him with ill-disguised impatience, "if you're going to murder me, there's not much I can do about it. If you're planning to rob me, I don't think you'll find it worth your trouble. And if it's rape you have on your mind, you may as well get it over with, because frankly I'm too tired to put up much of a fight, and the way things have been going for me today I really can't say I would even be surprised. The perfect end to a perfect day, you might say."

The corners of his lips deepened with suppressed mirth. "Now that," he murmured, "is what I call making me an offer I can't refuse."

She suddenly thought of her missed dinner and the

explanations she would have to make, and she was not in much of a mood for teasing.

"Oh, I'm not worried," she responded in a bored tone. "High-priced lawyers hardly ever get their kicks out of murdering and raping people—only robbing them."

He made a startled sound of suppressed laughter. "Lady, please!"

"My name is Lindsey," she reminded him somewhat acerbically, sitting up straighter as she prepared herself for battle. "And let me tell you something else, Mr. Psychopath—your lectures are wasted on me. I refuse to live my life circumscribed by fear. I have enough to worry about trying to remember to pay my bills on time and set my alarm clock at night and keep my checkbook balanced and"—she shot him a withering look—"take my car in for maintenance, and I don't need to borrow worries. I find," she finished decisively, "that people who go around looking for trouble generally find it, and that's one thing I don't need."

To her very great surprise, her improvised speech had the effect of silencing him on that subject, at least temporarily, and she thought she caught a hint of a peculiar sort of admiration in his brief glance. He moved on to a safer topic of conversation. "So," he inquired, "how long have you been in Atlanta?"

"Less than a week," she admitted, his casual tone soothing her ruffled temper somewhat. "It's been a pretty hectic week, too, and everything that happened tonight was just the icing on the cake. I'm starting a new job," she confessed with a sigh, "and tonight was supposed to be a sort of get-acquainted orientation dinner. I really hated to blow it."

He made no reply, and because she did not want the conversation to lag, she added, "I hope I'm not keeping you from an appointment. I mean, you must have come back to your office for something."

"Just to pick up some papers. Which way off the freeway?"

"Right. No, left. No wait a minute—I turned left onto the freeway..."

He gave her a patient look and suggested, "Just give me the name of the street."

She told him, and because the look he gave her was so much like that one would direct upon an incompetent child, she changed the subject again. "Were you running in the rain?"

"What?"

"You're dressed for running," she pointed out.

He made the turn—right, as she had first thought—and found the street with no difficulty, answering, "No, there's a health club near the office with an indoor track...." And then he looked at her and laughed. "Now you have me doing it! Telling you my life's story without thinking about it twice." He shook his head in wonder, and he looked more relaxed now than at any time since she had met him. She suspected he was the type of man who let his guard down only rarely, and she liked it so much when he laughed that she resolved to make him do it as often as possible...never thinking, at that moment, that their time together was almost up and that it was highly unlikely that she would ever see him again.

And then he directed a question to her, his tone still laced with amusement. "How old are you, anyway?"

"How old are you?" she retorted, recognizing the implication that she looked like a teenager. Her youthful appearance had been too much of a handicap in her professional—and sometimes social—life for her to consider it a compliment.

"I'm ninety-six," he replied immediately. "I know I don't look it, but that's all diet and exercise."

Now she laughed, and directed him to a group of attractive tudor-style apartment buildings. "I'm twenty-nine," she answered. "I know I don't look it, but—"

"That's simply your attitude of blind innocence toward the world and everything in it," he supplied. "Very refreshing," he added, glancing at her, "but not very healthy."

She did not know quite how to respond to that without getting into another argument, which, as he pulled up in front of her building, she knew they would not have a chance to complete satisfactorily. She decided to simply thank him and say good night, but as she turned he informed her, "I'll walk you to your door," and got out of the car.

She simply shrugged and allowed him to take her arm again as she got out of the car.

In the darkness of the eaves—she had forgotten to turn on the porch light—she fumbled in her purse for her keys. She came up with her car keys—totally useless now, she reflected dourly—a compact, folding comb, wallet...and about that time he interjected wryly, "Forgot your keys?"

She tried not to glare at him as she continued to search, and he reached forward and tried the doorknob. It opened when he twisted it. "It wasn't locked," he informed her.

"I—guess not," she admitted, relieved only that after everything else she was not going to have to try to break into her own apartment.

She started to step inside, saying, "Well, thank you for all your trouble—" But he restrained her with a meaningful look and a light touch on her arm. He preceded her, finding the light switch by the door and presumably checking for intruders.

"Oh, for goodness' sake!" she exclaimed, totally exasperated now. She followed him inside, tossing her purse on a cluttered chair and shrugging out of her jacket. "What is it with you and your obsession with crime? Are you some kind of undercover cop or something?"

"I spent four years with the D.A.'s office," he responded, his sweeping glance taking in every detail of the cluttered room, from the unhung draperies to the unmade bed, "prosecuting all sorts of criminals for all sorts of crimes. I also helped start a crime prevention program which, I like to think, raised our citizens' awareness a little. I don't like to be reminded how many people there are out there like you who must have totally ignored all our good advice and who even now"—he passed her a dry look—"are leaving their doors unlocked and their outside lights off and picking up strangers in deserted buildings."

"Now wait just a minute," she retaliated, incensed. "I did *not* pick you up! As a matter of fact—"

"Do you mind if I ask you a personal question?" he interrupted mildly, his gaze fixed on the two empty picture windows which, when she finished decorating, would be the highlights of the efficiency apartment. The gaily patterned draperies which were meant to cover them were stretched out on the floor beneath the sills. Without waiting for her reply, he inquired, "How do you get undressed?"

She faced him defiantly and retorted, "One leg at a time, thank you!"

His choked-off laugh of surprise was gratifying, and she informed him with slightly less rancor, "My *bathroom* doesn't have any windows, if you must know."

And then she became suddenly aware that his perceptive gaze was uncovering things she would not have wanted her best friend to see, much less a perfect stranger. Half-unpacked cartons and barrels littered the floor, and she automatically began to pick up wads of newsprint and shredded Styrofoam that covered the carpet. The wicker bed was tousled, revealing pretty pink floral sheets and pillow cases trimmed with wide borders of lace and, to her chagrin, the filmy blue nightgown she had worn to bed the night before. She had been in the process of arranging the contents of her dresser-drawers when Art's invitation to dinner had come, and as a result, a tangle of satiny underclothes trailed from the wicker rocking chair to the telephone stand across the room. A pair of panty-hose with a run in them decorated a lamp shade. Books and kitchen utensils mingled wantonly with the would-be contents of her linen closet and medicine chest, and not one available surface was free of boxes.

"My furniture just arrived yesterday," she explained hastily, removing a few of the more obvious pieces of personal clothing from his view. "I haven't had time to do much...."

"So I see." Politely, he handed the torn panty-hose to her, which she stuffed into a drawer with a subdued blush. And then he inquired, "I don't suppose you have anything to eat in the place?"

She looked at him in some confusion. First he had berated her for "picking up strangers," and then he invited himself to dinner. The very thought of her missed meal made her go almost weak with hunger. And the sensation only increased when she mentally calculated the contents of her kitchen as half a cup of yogurt, a pint of milk, and a box of cereal.

"I suppose I could make some coffee," she offered

hesitantly. After all, he had gone to a great deal of trouble for her and it was the least she could do. "You'll have to give me a minute to find the coffeepot, though...."

He shook his head in impatience mixed with amusement. "I was suggesting," he said, "that since neither of us had had dinner, we could do it together. Unless"—his eyes swept mockingly about the room—"you had other plans?"

She was both surprised and grateful for the invitation, and she didn't think twice about accepting. But she felt she had already imposed upon him so much that she had to insist, "Dutch. It's just that I'm so hungry, and I don't have my car, and you're right, there's not a thing to eat here. You've already done so much for me that I just wouldn't feel right about letting you take me out, too, so I insist upon paying for my meal—" And then she remembered her temporary shortage of cash and her spirits plummeted. She glanced at him in embarrassment. "Only..."

He seemed vastly entertained. "Most women," he told her, "accept a dinner invitation at face value and work out the terms of payment afterward. Now that's two you owe me. Be careful I don't start charging you interest."

She felt a pretty blush of confusion touch her cheeks, and that seemed to delight him. For a moment his eyes softened and just for that brief time she was reminded of the almost forgotten interlude on the elevator. He seemed at once all the things she had imagined him to be on first glance—tender, compassionate, warm. And then it was gone in a flash as he said briskly, "Only one problem. You're dressed for caviar and champagne and I"—he gestured to his sweatsuit—"am dressed for pizza and beer. Is there a compromise somewhere?"

"Pizza sounds great," she said quickly and hurried to her dresser. "I'll change."

"Mind if I use your phone?" he called as she reached the bathroom.

She answered, "Help yourself!" and closed the bathroom door.

She changed quickly into white jeans and a madras top, giving her hair a quick fluffing with the brush. She freshened her lipstick and removed her earrings, which were really too dressy for jeans, and as she did his voice floated to her through the thin walls of the apartment.

"Hi, sweetheart...." The exchange was very brief and to the point. "Yeah, I know. I got tied up." He laughed a little. "Well, because I found something better to do, of course! No, don't wait up, I'll see you some time tomorrow or the next day. I keep telling you there's no rush. Okay... take it easy now.... Love ya. 'Night babe."

Lindsey came out of the bathroom at a somewhat slower pace than she had entered, buttoning her sleeve, trying to look casual as he turned from the telephone. "Your wife," she inquired cautiously, "or your girl friend?"

His eyes gleamed with frank humor as he informed her, "My mother." He took her arm and guided her toward the door, pausing for her to collect her purse. "She's into real estate, and I'm handling a deal for her," he explained. "I was supposed to bring those papers over tonight, but I figured she had gotten me into enough trouble for one evening. She can wait."

She compressed her lips against a bubble of laughter as she glanced up at him, and the twinkle in his own eyes warmed her all over. He rested his hand lightly on her back as he pulled the door closed behind them.

They took a corner booth at a nearby pizza parlor and

helped themselves at the salad bar. Lindsey was so ravenous that she had finished half her salad before she even looked up, and when she did it was to find him watching her with lazy humor. "I feel guilty," he commented, reaching for his beer. "I should have made the offer earlier, but I didn't realize I had a starving waif on my hands."

Lindsey made a face at him as she touched her napkin to her lips. "I don't think I had any lunch," she admitted. "I guess that makes twice tonight you've rescued me—first from being stranded downtown without a car and now from starving to death."

"Terms still to be negotiated," he reminded her, saluting her with his glass, and she turned demurely back to her salad.

When the pizza was served he invited, "So tell me about Iowa. What did you do there?"

"I taught at the university in Cedar Falls," she answered, sliding a piece of pizza, thick with gooey cheese, onto her plate.

"Nice campus?"

"Umm." She waited until she finished the bite of pizza she had taken to inform him flippantly, "Twenty-four-hour security guard."

"I know you think I'm being dramatic," he told her seriously, "but any city with a population over ten thousand is going to have a significant crime problem. We can't just ignore it and hope it will go away. The bigger the city, the bigger the problem. I know about small towns—I was raised in one and I still spend a lot of my time traveling through the state. In Cedar Falls, I imagine, you might have had one or two murders a month and then it was headline news, right? Well, let me tell you something—here there are so many homicides every night that most of them don't even make the news... they're just statistics. And it's no different here than in Chicago or New York or Los Angeles, and when you consider that most of the population in this country is concentrated in those big cities, it becomes a very significant problem indeed. Those who aren't part of the solution are part of the problem. Just another statistic."

She sipped her Coke, recognizing that this was a subject about which he felt strongly. "And the solution is?" she prompted.

"That's a complicated subject," he admitted, the dark brows drawing together thoughtfully, "and one which can't be discussed adequately over dinner. But a good start on the solution is not to encourage crime through carelessness and ignorance. To prevent crime through self-defense."

Now he was hitting on a touchy subject for Lindsey, both politically and personally. She inquired with cautious restraint, "I take it you are against gun control?"

"That's really not a subject for debate," he replied mildly. "Gun control is blatantly unconstitutional."

"But," she pursued, trying very hard to remain impartial, "you wouldn't actually *own* a gun, would you?"

"I own," he informed her, cutting another slice of pizza, "exactly forty-four. I'm a collector."

She took another sip of her Coke and swallowed hard, trying to keep her tone conversational. "Handguns?"

"A few." He happened to glance up then, and at the expression of tight-lipped disapproval on her face, one corner of his mouth dropped wryly. "And, yes, at least one of them is loaded at all times and intended for use as a weapon."

She made a sound of muted exasperation and

turned briefly to stare out of the blackened window-pane. Then she turned back to him and exclaimed, "I really can't believe this! You seem like such an intelligent person! What about all the hundreds of children who die each year in handgun accidents? What about the accidental shootings and the domestic quarrels that end in murder? What about the utter *futility* of owning a gun? When an intruder comes into your home he's either desperate or determined, and the sight of a weapon is only going to frighten him into defending himself. Most people who confront an intruder with a gun are either too startled or too inexperienced to use it, while your criminal, on the other hand, has none of those handicaps. Not to mention the moral aspects—"

He interrupted her tirade with a gentle smile. "I see you're very well informed. And I must admit, you argue your case persuasively. I'm impressed. In my own defense, I can only point out that I have no children, my guns are accessible only to myself—"

"Ha!" she interrupted derisively. "Famous last words!"

"I'm a registered marksman certified in the use of handguns," he continued without pausing to acknowledge her comment, "*and* the matter of whether or not to own a gun is a very personal decision. The right to make that decision is all I'm interested in protecting."

She looked at him for a long time, and gradually the abrasive effects of the argument faded into a gentler emotion...something very much like pity. She said softly, without meaning to, "It must be terrible to live that way—suspicious of everyone and everything. Always expecting the worst, not trusting anyone."

He had turned back to his pizza, but now he looked up, and the first expression in his eyes was almost star-

tled. It changed quickly, however, into one of simple
bafflement, and he commented, "I'm not sure I follow
you."

She lifted her shoulders lightly and tried to explain.
"It's just that when I see a stranger on the street, I see a
potential friend, you see a potential enemy. When I
leave the house in the morning, I think about all the
good things that are going to happen; you think of all
the dangers. I know it sounds unsophisticated," she admitted, dropping her eyes and shaking her head a little,
"but I couldn't live like that."

Silence fell, and when she looked up again she was
surprised by the expression on his face. He was looking
at her intently, but it was an absent, almost unseeing
look—the look of someone who has been confronted
with a truth about himself and startled into speechless-
ness by it. There was sadness there, too, almost a
yearning in the depth of his eyes, and a softness about
his mouth that drew Lindsey into an immediate em-
pathy with him. She knew that she had found that part
of him she had first sensed on the elevator; she felt a
closeness with him and a mutuality, and she wanted to
explore it further. But then the lines of his face
smoothed out into an easy smile, the softness of his
eyes faded, and he leaned back against the booth saying
simply, "Well done." There was mockery in his tone
and in the twist of his lips. "But, if I might simply say, I
can think of much more interesting topics to discuss
over a candlelit table across from a lovely lady."

She was disappointed to lose the moment, but she
tried not to let it show as she shifted uncomfortably in
her seat. "Like what?"

He leaned his chin on his fist and examined her features with a slow deliberation which drove all thoughts
of their previous topic of conversation out of her head

under the impact of new, pleasantly unexpected sensations. "Like," he suggested, "your freckles. Are they just on your nose, or all over your body?"

Her blush caught her unawares, and she brought her hand briefly to the bridge of her nose to cover it. In the dancing red candlelight her eyes sparkled with repressed laughter. "That," she retorted, "is an invasion of privacy."

He laughed and sat back, taking up another slice of pizza.

By the time they left the restaurant Lindsey found it hard to believe that her companion was the same man she had originally met on the elevator. Though they talked of inconsequential things—staying carefully away from personal and controversial subjects—he seemed relaxed and at ease. In this mood she found him to be sharp-witted and quick to laugh, charming and easy to be with. She was sorry when he walked her to her door again and it was time to say goodnight.

She invited impulsively, "I think I could find the coffeepot if you would like to come in for a few minutes." She tried the doorknob, adding quickly, "That is, unless you have to get home—" She interrupted herself with the exclamation, "It's locked!" And she rattled the doorknob again futilely.

"Of course," he told her with a slight frown.

"But I don't have my keys!" she cried but began a futile search through her purse anyway. "I didn't know you were going to lock the door—we weren't going to be gone long—you should have reminded me to take the keys, you knew I didn't have them...."

He gave her a look heavy with forebearance and tinged with amusement as he inquired, "I don't suppose you have a hairpin on you?"

She simply returned his look blankly, and he shook his head in resignation, stepping forward to grasp the doorknob beneath her fingers. With a quick twisting movement and an upward jerk, he tapped the wood just above the doorknob with his fist, and the door sprang open. He gave her a sardonic glance. "I suggest you look into the possibility of new locks."

She looked from him to the open door in muted amazement and murmured, "*Now* I understand your expertise on the subject of crime. You were a burglar before you were a lawyer, right?"

He declined to answer, gesturing her inside with a sweep of his arm.

"First," he ordered, closing the door behind them, "get your keys and put them in your purse. Then forget the coffee and bring me a hammer. We've got work to do."

She slipped out of her jacket, staring at him as he crossed the room toward the windows. "What for?" she demanded. "What kind of work?"

He took up a length of drapery from the floor and replied without turning, "I haven't forgotten your invitation to spend the night, and I'm not an exhibitionist."

She experienced just a second of real alarm, but she caught the twinkle in his eye just in time. "I think I've been misquoted," she retorted pertly. "I may have been known to pick up a stranger or two in my time, but I never go to bed with them . . . not on the first date, anyway."

"My, my," he murmured, turning back to the windows. "The future looks brighter all the time."

But for the next half hour it was business only, while they were in the process of hanging the draperies, and when at last Lindsey cleared off a space on the sofa to admire their handiwork, she was surprised when he did not join her. Instead he simply bent down and grasped her hands, pulling her to her feet. "I have a nine-o'clock appointment in the morning," he said, "and I've really got to be going. But first," he added in a perfectly impersonal, slightly brisk tone, "there's the matter of my bill to be settled."

It happened so quickly Lindsey did not have a chance to see it coming; certainly she wouldn't have guessed that he could go so quickly from business to ardor—or even teasing—without warning. She felt his hands slide to her waist, and she was pulled against him gently, and in that last moment she suspected that even he had no intention of doing anything other than teasing her.

But then that devastating sexual chemistry flared with his first touch; without her being aware of it her hands were against the soft material of his sweatsuit on his chest, and he was kissing her. The softness of his lips upon hers generated an immediate and uncontrollable response in her; she felt a tingling surge of warmth throughout her body which escalated in sweeping peaks until she actually felt dizzy. She felt as though she was melting into him; she was no longer aware of breathing, but there was a dull ache in her chest. And then it was over as abruptly as it had begun.

For a moment her head swam in confusion and she dropped her eyes, ashamed to have him see what a devastating effect his intended playfulness had had on her. His hands lingered on her waist and where his fingers touched was a searing heat; the rest of her felt empty yet expectant. She thought she felt his fingers tighten once, as though in a moment of indecision, and then she became aware that his eyes were upon her and she raised her own to meet them hesitantly.

He looked as dazed as she felt. For once, there were

no defenses, no flippancy in his smile, no hardness in his eyes. And he said, very softly, "I think I've been overpaid."

She tried to return his smile, hesitantly, but in a moment she dropped her eyes again in confusion. What was she to think, after all? He was a perfect stranger; she was not at all sure she even liked him, and things like this did not usually happen to her....

And then, forcefully, he released his hold on her waist and stepped back. When she looked at him it was as though a different person had stepped into his place. Gone were the gentleness, the unsteady signs of restrained passion, the *humanness* she had witnessed so intimately a moment before. His face was impersonal, his eyes remote, though not unfriendly, and his tone brisk. The transformation had the effect of draining the hot color from her cheeks and stilling her wild heartbeat so abruptly it was painful, and she simply stared at him, feeling bereft and numb with amazement.

"I'll pick you up at seven in the morning," he said, moving toward the door. "We'll see what we can do about your car."

"Y-yes," she managed bleakly, trailing after him. "Thank you ... for all your trouble, I mean ... and for dinner...." She ran out of things to say. She could not even think.

"Lock your door," he reminded her, and he was gone.

Chapter Three

Lindsey stirred groggily the next morning to the sound of a faraway pounding. She opened her eyes a slit, but the room was fully dark, and she moaned and pulled the pillow over her head, thinking something vaguely about noisy neighbors. The pounding continued, and half-dozing memories of the night before began to seep through: the missed dinner, being trapped in the elevator, her broken car, and interlude with a dark-eyed stranger which must surely be part of a romantic dream. . . .

Her car! She sat bolt upright in bed, fully awake, her eyes riveting on her clock in alarm. It was just after seven and it hadn't been a dream at all. . . . She scrambled out of bed, almost tripping over the covers that became entwined in her feet, and made her way quickly to the door, stumbling over boxes and bumping her shin against the coffee table in the darkened room. She flung open the door and bent to rub her bruised shin, and when she looked up Trey was leaning against the doorframe, frowning down at her in disapproval. "Don't you know what a safety chain is for?" he demanded.

"Will you come off that?" she returned, somewhat disgruntled herself. "I knew it was you!"

"If you knew it was me," he retorted, stepping inside and closing the door, "why did you let me stand out there knocking for five minutes?"

"I overslept," she mumbled, groping for the light switch. "The sun usually wakes me up. I forgot about the draperies."

The room sprang into light, and Lindsey stood there, blinking and pushing her hair out of her eyes while Trey's eyes swept over her in leisurely appreciation. She was wearing a floral-printed baby-doll nightgown with short puffed sleeves and a ruffled scooped neckline, which afforded him a fine view of slender white legs and the lace-trimmed edges of her bikini panties. She would have run for a robe if she could remember where she had put it, but she spared herself an undignified frantic search by returning his stare coolly and commenting, "You look very nice this morning, too."

Slowly, he grinned, acknowledging with a glint of admiration in his eye her successful struggle against embarrassment. He told her, "I'm also going to be late if you don't hurry."

He was wearing a camel-colored three-piece suit, which on another man would have looked very Wall Street, stuffy and pretentious. The effect upon him was of casual elegance, from the negligent arrangement of his slightly long, thick brown hair to the small gold cufflinks at his wrists. She remembered his mentioning an appointment last night, and said quickly, "It will just take me a minute, I promise. I'm sorry you had to wait; I'll hurry."

She scrambled through her drawer for underclothes and scooped a day outfit from the closet, inviting as she hurried past on her way to the bathroom, "Have a seat. I'll be right back."

"Where?" he called after her, and she shut the bathroom door.

She made the change in record time, stripping off her

nightgown for a pair of pale blue slacks and a matching cardigan set in a light, nubby weave. She splashed cold water on her face and ran a brush through her hair, grimacing at herself in the mirror and wondering if she dared take time to put on a little makeup. As a rule, she wore nothing but lip gloss and a little eye color, but she supposed it was a natural feminine instinct to want to look her best when a man was present. She doubted, however, that this man would be as impressed by her appearance as he would be by promptness.

Her mouth was full of toothpaste when the phone began to ring. It rang three times before he called, "Shall I answer it?"

She called back, "Please!" without thinking, and when she realized what she had done, she froze. Only one person would be calling her, only one person knew her number, and what would he think...?

She rinsed her mouth and rushed from the bathroom, but too late. Trey was holding out the phone to her, a wicked little smile tugging at the corners of his lips. He said simply, "It's for you."

And there went her hopes that it might be a wrong number. She swallowed hard and took the steps to him slowly, dreading the upcoming conversation. She had enough to explain to Art already without having her morals dragged into the question. But she ventured anyway, "Who is it?"

He handed the phone to her, his eyes sparkling madly as he struggled to keep his expression deadpan. "He didn't say."

She took a breath, brought the phone to her ear, and spoke into it cautiously.

Art's voice exploded at her. "What the hell is a man doing answering your phone at seven o'clock in the morning? I thought you said you didn't know anyone in town! Is *that* what happened to you last night?"

She winced and turned away from Trey's amused gaze. She knew there was no point in trying to explain it to him now. "Listen," she said tiredly, "it's a long story—"

"I'll just bet it is! You've got thirty seconds," he challenged her.

"I got lost, stuck in an elevator, and my car broke down," she told him.

For a moment there was dead silence, then he drawled, "One excuse was all I needed. Don't strain your imagination. And who was the fellow on the phone?"

"He's taking me to pick up my car. Not," she added somewhat bitingly, quickly turning the tables on him, "that I have to account to you for who does or does not answer my phone after you left me stranded downtown with no car and no money and not even a telephone number where I could reach you?"

"*I* left *you*! You were over an hour late!" A breath, and his tone changed. "Wait a minute. Are we about to have one of those sibling brawls I hear so much about?"

"Quite possibly," she returned loftily, though she relaxed as she sensed his anger change to amusement.

For a moment there was silence, then he inquired, "Did you really get stuck in an elevator?"

"What do you think?"

He sighed. "I think you probably did." Then, "We need to see you at campaign headquarters in an hour. Can you possibly, by any stretch of the imagination, make it?"

"Give me two hours."

"Shall I send an armored truck?"

"Not necessary," she retorted.

"What about your car—"

She hung up the phone.

She turned to Trey with a calm, faintly triumphant smile. "Shall we go?"

He inclined his head to her, disguising the twinkle in his eye, and opened the door. He paused before closing the door behind them to inquire, "Do you have your keys?"

Her sense of victory faded abruptly and she went meekly back inside to get her purse.

Trey avoided most of the morning traffic by taking the side streets, and the scenery was resplendent, as only an early April morning can make it. As they moved closer to midtown, stately colonial mansions and sprawling brick structures dominated lawns shadowed in every conceivable shade of green, highlighting the artistry of flower beds filled with tulips and jonquils and banks covered in baby's breath or the purple-blossomed thrift plant. Dewy pink and white dogwood lined the streets along with the delicate white and pale green of a blossoming apple tree here and there. Flame azaleas in passion pink and fire red clustered around thick-trunked oaks and lined walkways; everywhere was such a riot of color and the delicate perfume of a soft spring morning that Lindsey strained to take it all in, sighing at last, "Isn't it beautiful?" She turned to Trey, eyes shining, to share her enthusiasm. "We never see anything like this out West. I mean, isn't it just beautiful?"

He lifted a shoulder noncommittally. "You wouldn't believe the drop in productivity, city-wide, these first few weeks of April." He glanced at her, and explained, "Pollen. It's become a real problem in the work force. People who've never had hay fever before take to their beds for a week at a time. Every other person you pass on the street is either sneezing or coughing. You have to wash your car every day." Again he shrugged. "There's a price for everything, I guess."

She stared at him, amazed at his ability to take the romance and adventure out of something as innocently beautiful as the view, and she responded dryly, "How very poetic."

He glanced at her, one brow quirked slightly, and she knew he was enjoying irritating her. "Ah," he said softly, "you want poetry. I suppose I should say mornings like this always remind me of weddings. That on a morning like this all a man could wish for is a picnic lunch in the back seat and a pretty girl by his side." Again he glanced at her. "And I suppose I should also say I have everything but the picnic lunch."

"You also," she reminded him, turning back to the window, "have an appointment."

"See?" he responded mildly. "I would have done just as well to have stuck with the subject of pollen."

She suppressed a giggle and fixed her gaze determinedly on the view.

Her little car still sat there, though it looked not so forlorn as it had when they left it in the deserted garage last night. The parking level was almost full when they arrived, and the building echoed with the magnified roar of engines and slamming car doors and co-workers calling greetings to each other.

"Just let me have a look under the hood," Trey said as they got out, "but I don't think we'll have any trouble with it this morning."

Lindsey slid behind the wheel and waited as he opened the hood. Then she was aware of two men approaching the car. "Good morning!" They were addressing Trey, not her. "Having trouble?"

Trey glanced up. "Just helping out a lady in distress," he responded as they reached him. Lindsey noticed that he did not bother to introduce her...not, she assured herself, that she should expect him to.

"Need any help?" one of the men inquired. They

were both dressed in business suits and Lindsey assumed they were lawyer-friends of his.

"I think we've got it under control." He stepped around the front of the car and signaled Lindsey to try the engine. It started on the first turn, and for some very peculiar reason Lindsey was disappointed.

"Go on up and have a cup of coffee," Trey invited his two friends. "I'll be with you in a minute." He closed the hood.

As they left, each of them turned to smile at her, and then Trey came around to her window, wiping his hands on a handkerchief. "Go directly to a garage," he instructed her, "and order a complete tune-up. Did this car really make it all the way from Iowa?"

"I can't," she told him. "I have to meet my brother this morning. But I will...as soon as I get a chance."

"Don't say I didn't warn you," he replied. "Your good luck and good looks may not get you through next time."

She did not know quite how to respond to this and was ashamed of the warm feelings such an offhand compliment could generate. She knew that this was where they said good-bye, and she was hoping, foolishly, she knew, that it would not be permanent. But because she did not know how to communicate that hope to him and because it was evident in his face that he was anxious to be away, she found herself saying simply, "You've been so kind. Thank you—for all your trouble..." It came out as a formal platitude, not at all the way she wanted to express her feelings, but there was really nothing else she could say. And he was already nodding and turning away, with nothing more for her than a backward wave of his hand.

She put her car into gear, swallowing her disappointment, and then he turned. "Oh—Lindsey." He was walking back to her. She looked up expectantly.

He took something out of his wallet; she was certain he was going to ask her to write down her phone number, or at the very least, give her his card. But he only said, with another wry twist to his tone, "I don't suppose you've had a chance to go to the bank. Use my pass to get out of the garage, and just leave it with the attendant, will you?"

She took the laminated card he gave her slowly, her disappointment so thick it almost choked her and made it very difficult for her to smile her thanks. "I—I didn't think about that," she admitted.

His lips tightened cynically. "Of course not."

"I'll leave it with the attendant," she assured him. "Thanks—again."

"You're welcome...again."

He turned and started for the door, and he did not look back again as Lindsey maneuvered out of the parking space and started for the exit.

She presented Trey's pass to the attendant and asked for directions to Spring Street, where Addison Cantrell's campaign headquarters was located. But she was only half attentive as she followed those directions, for most of her thoughts were occupied with the man she left behind.

She could not understand the letdown feeling which was seeping through her at the realization she would never see him again. In the course of her job and through her own out-going personality, Lindsey met hundreds of new people every year, and it wasn't unusual for her to forget a face as soon as it was out of sight. The encounter with Trey was not so different from a dozen others...yet it was different. For now she was left with a sense of emptiness, of an adventure unfulfilled, as though she had missed her destiny by inches.

She gave herself a little shake of reprimand for the

romantic exaggeration of her thoughts and tried to concentrate on driving. She didn't even know his last name. They were miles apart in their thinking and their values and their attitudes toward life, and if she were to be perfectly frank, he was not an altogether pleasant person. She knew nothing about him and liked very little of what she did know, but still...she wished she had had the chance to know him better.

Lindsey had had many male friends, but few lovers. Most men automatically looked upon her as the sister they had never had or wished they had or had grown away from and wished they hadn't. Those few times she had allowed herself to be drawn into a romantic affair it had been acknowledged by both parties from the outset that nothing permanent was intended, that it wasn't serious. Lindsey grew tired of that sort of meaningless encounter very quickly, for it only served to remind her that there must be something more to the man-woman relationship than a respite from boredom, good times to fill the empty places. Lindsey had never been deeply touched emotionally or sensually, and on this spring morning, awash with pastel colors and nature's delicate perfume, she felt the lack acutely.

She shrugged irritably and told herself, *It's spring, and a young woman's fancy turns to thoughts of—* And then she realized that she had passed the building toward which she had been heading, and she made an abrupt and rather reckless left-hand turn to circle the block again.

The difference was that he had kissed her. It was true that she did not know him and probably would not like him if she did and that he had most likely already forgotten her name, but he had kissed her and that made all the difference. She was not old-fashioned enough to attach undue significance to a simple kiss, but neither was she the type of girl who generally allowed herself to be kissed by strangers. Something had happened between them, there was no use denying that now, and it was something that had never happened to Lindsey before. Perhaps it was a common enough experience for him—after all, just because a man kisses a girl does not necessarily obligate him to ever call her again—but for Lindsey something had changed when he had taken her into his arms. When he had kissed her, all she could think about was making love with him, and she supposed if he had asked her she would have gone to bed with him last night.

That was a rather shocking admission for Lindsey, and her cheeks were stained red as she swung into the parking lot across the street. The color in her cheeks was from both annoyance with and amazement at herself, but the warmth which tingled in her fingertips was from a memory. It must, she thought dryly as she got out and slammed the car door, be something in the pollen.

Both Addison and Art were there to greet her when she walked into the office. Typewriters and photocopiers were going madly, manned by some dozen volunteers; stacks of posters and leaflets were piled upon long tables and desks and in every available corner of floor space; and larger-than-life likenesses of Addison Cantrell smiled down at her benevolently from every wall. It was the familiar chaos Lindsey knew so well, the bustle and confusion which set her adrenaline to flowing and quickened her senses for a challenge, and from the moment she stepped into the room everything else was forgotten.

Uncle Addison reached her first and enfolded her in an exuberant embrace. "I was beginning to think you were a figment of my imagination, my dear!" he exclaimed. "You look wonderful!"

Addison Cantrell was a portly man, florid-faced and balding. He smelled familiarly of a woodsy cologne and rich cigars; he exuded comfort and fatherliness, which were as much a part of his voter appeal as was his exemplary record on the Senate floor. Embracing Uncle Addison was for Lindsey always like hugging a worn and dearly loved teddy bear, filled with warm childhood memories and all the security of home. She laughed out loud with the pure pleasure of seeing him again.

He stepped back to hold her at arm's length, his eyes twinkling, and he said, "I can't tell you how glad I am that you made it—and all in one piece."

"And only ten minutes late," added Art.

"I'm sorry I missed your first night in town," she started to explain.

"Arthur mentioned that you had a little...trouble." A dancing glance was passed to Art, and she knew they had been laughing about it all morning.

"It really wasn't my fault," she defended, anxious to have them know that on this occasion at least she had been totally a victim of circumstance.

Addison chuckled and squeezed her hands. "My dear, I wouldn't have you any other way." Then he turned and, still holding her hands, announced to the room: "Everyone, this is Lindsey Madison. She will be my second-in-command when Arthur isn't here, and I want you all to give her your best cooperation. You can all introduce yourselves later, right now we've got work to do."

She received several smiles and nods before the others returned to their work, and Uncle Addison draped his arm about her shoulders as he led her toward a private office near the back. "I haven't told you how much I appreciate your coming, Lindsey," he said.

"It's never easy joining a campaign in the middle, and I know it was a sacrifice for you."

"Not at all," she denied quickly. "You know I jumped at the chance. I had leave coming, and it was no problem getting someone else to finish out the term for me."

"It was a risk," he told her, "not renewing your contract."

She laughed. "Life is full of risks!"

They paused by the desk of one middle-aged woman whose graying brown hair was pulled back into a thin ponytail and who was almost lost beneath a pile of papers. Addison dropped his hand onto the woman's shoulder affectionately. "Now this is one person you want to make friends with real fast. She holds the key to this entire operation—not to mention the file cabinets, stamp machine, and photocopiers. Louise, this is my niece, Lindsey Madison."

The woman smiled up at her. "Anything I can do to help, Miss Madison, you just let me know. We're all on the same team here."

Lindsey returned her smile and said, "Call me Lindsey. And I'll be sure to take you up on your offer."

Addison inquired with an endearing grin, "If I ask nicely, do you suppose you could be persuaded to bring an old man a cup of coffee?"

"I might have to make a fresh pot, Mr. Cantrell," responded Louise, starting to rise. "Everyone seems to have had a little trouble waking up this morning."

"Whenever you get a chance," replied Addison, waving her back to her seat.

"I have a chance right now," she told him firmly, inching past, and Addison exchanged a conspiratorial look with Art.

"You see that, young man?" he demanded. "You just have to let these women know who's boss." He squeezed Louise's arm as he opened the door to the inner office. "You're a treasure, Louise."

Lindsey knew already that her primary functions would be as speechwriter and asssistant to Art, who was the official campaign manager. Art would be traveling with Uncle Addison on the campaign trail, and in the heat of the campaign, Lindsey would be left to anchor everything from headquarters. Of course she had done her homework, and she was thoroughly familiar with the basics of the campaign, but she had a lot of catching up to do on the details. The basic groundwork had been laid over a year ago, and as Addison had pointed out, it wasn't easy coming in on the middle of a campaign.

Before delving into the issues, however, Addison gestured her to a comfortable chair near the window and perched informally on the edge of his desk. Art took a seat on the other side of the room, preparing to be, for the moment, a dispassionate observer.

Addison said seriously, "Again, Lindsey, thank you for coming. This campaign is going to be a bit more complicated than we thought at first, or I never would have asked you."

"I'm glad you did," she said quickly. "As a matter of fact, *I* should be thanking you."

He smiled a little. "Thank your brother. He's the one who reminded me that we had exactly the sort of talent we needed right in the family. Loyalty has become a very rare commodity, Lindsey," he added somewhat soberly, "at home as well as in Washington. If the truth be told, I've needed someone like you on my staff for a long time, but I've been afraid to ask you."

She looked up at him, puzzled. "But why? You know I've been wanting to go to Washington since my first campaign.... I've certainly hinted to you often enough!"

He smiled a little sadly. "Be patient with an old man, my dear. I knew you wanted Washington, but I wasn't sure it was the best thing for you. I didn't think you were ready, and if I may be perfectly frank, I still don't."

She made a small sound of impatience. "Uncle Addison—"

He held up a hand to silence her and told her, "Don't accuse me of treating you like a child, because in many ways that's exactly what you are, and you know it as well as I. Lindsey," he told her soberly, "more illusions are crushed on Capitol Hill in a single day than in a lifetime in Cedar Falls. A week in Washington and you'll be twenty years older and, selfishly, I don't want to see that happen to you."

Her expression softened. "Uncle Addison, I appreciate your concern, really I do. But I'm a big girl now. I've been working in politics for ten years and I know it's not all hearts and flowers. Give me a little credit; I can take care of myself in Washington or anywhere else. And," she added shrewdly, "if you didn't think so you wouldn't have asked me in the first place."

He sighed. "Again, that's pure selfishness. I need you up there. But please, Lindsey," he added sincerely, "don't go into this thing with the idea that you're going to change the system in twenty-four hours or less. I've been trying for twelve years and my successes can be counted on the fingers of one hand. I don't want to see you hurt."

She simply gave him a complacent smile.

Addison turned his eyes to Art, who only gave a disinterested shrug. "I told you, she's got a one-track mind. You couldn't get me within ten miles of that town, but Washington and Lindsey..." He shrugged. "Maybe they deserve each other."

She gave him a mirthless smile, but allowed herself a moment to wonder again over her brother's attitude.

Art had been groomed for political office since his first day at college, and he would have made such a perfect candidate for almost anything for which he decided to run that it had come as something of a shock to everyone concerned when he had decided he preferred life behind the scenes—and when he had remained firm with that decision. He had managed Uncle Addison's first senatorial campaign, and it had been after that that he had told Lindsey simply, "I'd rather be a kingmaker than a king. It's a lot safer." It puzzled Lindsey, but, then, Art was a veritable patchwork of contradictory traits and conflicting ambitions.

Lindsey's mother had died when Lindsey was two and Art was eight. Their father had managed quite well, all things considered, and there had never been any doubt of his love for them. Lindsey remembered an early childhood filled with happiness and adventure, a big burly man who made her squeal with delight at his enthusiastic demonstrations of affection, long walks in the woods, and the quiet times at sunset when her father would sit for hours gazing at nothing and exuding contentment. She could not remember wanting for anything; she learned later, of course, that they had wanted for almost everything but love.

Lindsey's father was a sculptor, unrecognized and unwanted in those early days, and his first loyalty had always been to things ethereal. As a result they had lived from hand to mouth, mending and patching, never being quite certain where their next meal was coming from. They moved from one small house to another on an average of three times a year, which was an adventure for Lindsey. She learned later, of course, that those moves were generally necessitated by a shortage of funds while her father was between paying jobs. Those paying jobs were so varied and so short-lived that Lindsey soon began to believe there was nothing her father could not do, from painting houses to fixing automobiles, and she had supported her father's genius to her brother during many heated arguments throughout their adolescent years—arguments which her father sublimely ignored in the determined pursuit of his art.

By the time Art graduated from high school, their father was beginning to receive some recognition of his work and to make money from it—enough to educate both his children at the finest universities and to allow him to retire from commercial success to again pursue his own ideas of artistic perfection. He now lived in a windswept cottage on the coast of South Carolina and had become something of a local legend. He produced one or two fine sculptures a year, which were collected by the very rich and very status conscious, and he enjoyed his reputation as an eccentric. Those early years of living from dream to dream had formed Lindsey into the woman she was today: idealistic and optimistic, caring more for ideas than possessions, adaptable and adventurous. But on Art they had had the exact opposite effect. She suspected that somewhere along the line he had determined never to return to the dusty shacks and one-course meals of his childhood, and he had developed a fierce passion for success. Everything about him, from his tailored suits to his expensively furnished apartment, spoke of an acute awareness of the status he projected. He chose his friends just as he chose his furnishings, always with an eye on usefulness and impressions. He was ambitious yet insecure, and sometimes it was that trait—a ruthless determination to achieve his goals but an unwillingness to take any risks in doing so—which frightened Lindsey about her brother. It did not occur to her that that was also precisely what made him so valuable on any political committee.

"Well," said Addison briskly, "all this talk about Washington is going to be purely academic unless we get busy and win this election."

Lindsey feigned surprise. "Is there any doubt that we will?"

Addison laughed and squeezed her shoulder before going around the desk to sit down. "Just what I need—unqualified optimism! I told you it was a good idea to bring her here, Art!"

Art pulled his chair closer to the desk, now in his element. "First, let's fill her in on the competition."

"What about the issues?" countered Lindsey. "First things first."

Art waved her suggestion away. "If you don't know the issues by now, you never will. Nothing new—taxes, abortion, crime, states' rights..."

"The real problem," said Addison, "is that issues are going to take second place to personalities in this campaign. I mean, what can you say about crime except that you're against it? Any politician knows how to get around the public on taxes and abortion, and my stand on states' rights is crystal clear." As he spoke he began pulling out folders crammed with drafts and copies of bills he had authored, voting records, publicity releases, and other relevant material which he spread before Lindsey.

Lindsey studied the papers, inquiring absently, "All right, so what does the competition look like?"

"About six two," answered Art, "one hundred seventy pounds, dark hair..."

Lindsey glanced at him. "Good looking?"

He relaxed long enough to grin at her. "Not my type."

"I think," chuckled Addison, "Arthur is referring to young Sinclair, the only thing the opposition has produced who has a chance in the primary. When it comes down to one-on-one, he's the man we'll be dealing with."

Louise came in just then with the coffee, and Lindsey sat back. "So how much of a threat is he?"

Addison shook his head slowly. "Two months ago, no one even knew who he was. Now it seems he's all you hear about. It always makes me a little nervous when someone comes on that strong this early in a campaign."

"Excuse me, Miss Madison," Louise interrupted, "how do you like your coffee?"

"Black, thank you," responded Lindsey absently, now fully concentrating on the details of the campaign.

Addison chuckled as he accepted his cup. "If I'm not careful, Sinclair will be stealing Louise away from me."

"If I were twenty years younger, maybe," she retorted playfully, and then volunteered, "I could put together a profile on Sinclair for you, Miss Madison, if that would help."

"Good idea," agreed Addison. "You need to know what we're up against. But," he told Louise, "there's no rush on it today. Have it ready for her Monday, and the two of you can spend the day scouting the enemy camp."

"The trouble is," said Art when she was gone, "there aren't that many issues we're divided on. It's like Addison said, it's going to come down to a battle of personalities, and I hate to say it, but all Sinclair has to do is step in front of a TV camera and he's got the vote of every woman within viewing range. He opens his mouth and he has every voter under the age of thirty right in the palm of his hand. A real smooth talker."

"On behalf of the women and youth of America,"

Lindsey murmured, not looking up from her papers, "I protest. Give us a little credit."

She finished the page she was reading and sat back thoughtfully. "It seems to me," she said, "that politicians in that genre burn out pretty quickly. You have to have more than charm on your side when it comes right down to the hard facts of swaying a cynical public. And he may not realize it, but he could be his own worst handicap. Too liberal, and you scare off the serious voters. Too conservative, and you look like a phony. Not to mention the fact that people like that tend to trip over their own shoestrings when it comes to keeping their reputations clean. The press goes for the throat when they see a person with that kind of media appeal, and he'll end up with a lapful of bad publicity before he even realizes the honeymoon is over."

"Nice theory," agreed Art cynically, "but not so in this case. He's squeaky clean through and through. The man could make an Eagle Scout look like a delinquent. If he has a private life it's *very* private, and his public record looks like a textbook. If I didn't know better, I'd think he had been programming his entire life just for this Senate race."

Lindsey glanced at him with new interest. "You know him?"

Art laughed shortly. "That man has slaughtered me so many times on the courtroom floor that it hurts to even think about it! His office was next to mine when he first went into private practice," he added, "but he's moved up since then. We played golf a couple of times." His brows drew together thoughtfully as he remembered those long-ago occasions. "I remember liking him, even though I did think he was a damn fool. He had a head full of idealistic nonsense and not a shred of ambition." He looked back to Lindsey. "His family is old money. River-Fresh Foods."

"And there goes the agricultural vote," sighed Addison.

"Not necessarily," put in Lindsey. "After all, what can a corporation like River-Fresh know about the small farmer? That can be a handicap."

"Maybe," replied Addison noncommittally. "The thing you have to remember, Lindsey, is that this man is a complete tool of the party. That's what makes him so dangerous. We're playing in the big leagues now."

"He's running this campaign like a military battle," agreed Art, "conquering factions one by one. First the women, because they're easiest"—Lindsey scowled at him—"then the young people, because they're the most active—"

"Most of Uncle Addison's supporters have always been under thirty-five," Lindsey interrupted. "He's going to have a fight on his hands if he expects to take them away."

Art turned a bland look on her. "Do you know who's appearing at a fund-raising dinner for Sinclair next month? Two hundred dollars a plate?" He named a popular rock group and Lindsey let her breath whistle slowly through her teeth.

"I wouldn't mind seeing them, myself," she murmured, and Addison gave an exaggerated groan.

They laughed together, and then Lindsey sat back, taking up her coffee. "You just leave Sinclair to me," she said confidently. "I'm sure you don't have anything to worry about from a man half your age and with none of your experience. You just remember," she told her uncle with a wink, "I've got a stake in this election, too. We are *not* going to lose."

The two men looked at one another, and with a shared smile, gradually gave in to her indefatigable confidence. Lindsey knew she had been welcomed to the team.

Chapter Four

It was typical of Uncle Addison to feel as though he owed her a meal after the missed dinner of the night before, and the three of them had lunch in the elegant Polaris Room atop the Hyatt Regency. Looking down over the city from the slowly rotating dining room, Lindsey's enthusiasm only mounted, and she had no doubt they could conquer the world.

She wanted to get right back to headquarters and delve into her work, but Addison insisted she take the rest of the day to finish unpacking and to settle her personal affairs. Monday would be her first full day of work, and after that there would be no time for distractions. She reluctantly admitted that she could use the time, and found herself planning an energetic schedule for the afternoon, which would include going to the bank, shopping for groceries, taking her car to the garage, and unpacking and arranging her furniture.

As they reached the parking lot where Lindsey had left her car, Addison said good-bye and left for the first of a series of appointments he had scheduled that afternoon. Art walked her to her car, draping his arm casually across her shoulders. "So. Tell me about that dude who answered your phone this morning. Hot night in the city, hmm?"

She scowled at him. "Really, Arthur, get your mind out of the gutter. He was just being friendly, that's all."

"I'll bet."

She looked up just in time to see she was being ruthlessly teased. "There are," she retorted loftily, "a few nice people left in this world. Of course *you* wouldn't know any of them."

"According to you," he drawled as they reached her car, "every unlikely-looking character you meet on the street is a nice person. I'm here to tell you, my dear, that's not necessarily so."

She was struck suddenly by how much that sentiment reminded her of Trey. Were all the men in her life fated to be cynical and suspicious? "Yeah, I know," she murmured dryly as she got into the car. "Don't talk to strangers."

"And be careful what you say to your friends." His easy grin faded as he leaned on her window, a sober look came into his eyes, and he told her, "Lindsey, I'm not one to harp on things, but you came here with your eyes wide open, didn't you? I never told you it was going to be easy."

She nodded. He had not misled her in any way, but her own optimism had neutralized his every warning. The opportunity had been too great for her to back away from it for any reason.

"We've got a hell of a fight on our hands, hon," he said, "and I'm counting on you. I just wanted you to know that."

She smiled at him, an easy affection surfacing for the brother she had never really understood but always loved. "No problem," she assured him cheerfully. "I didn't come this far to lose."

His lips tightened into what might have been a smile, or it might have been a grimace. "Just," he said very quietly, "don't be afraid to fight dirty."

The smile faded from her eyes, she drew in her breath to reply, but before she could, his own expression had changed and he inquired lightly, "Do you want to do something this weekend? Have dinner? See the sights?"

She relaxed in some confusion but managed another smile for him. "Do you have the time?"

"I'll make the time," he assured her, tugging at a strand of her hair playfully. He straightened up and added, "I'll give you a call tomorrow, okay?"

"Great."

He started to walk away, but then turned and added mischievously, "Think you can find your way home?"

She started her engine. "Good-bye, Art."

When she swung out of the parking place he was standing there, grinning, his hands shoved into his pockets, presumably watching to see whether or not she made the correct turn. She started to make a face at him, then she stepped on the brakes, suddenly remembering. "Art," she called, "do you have any money? I need it to get out of the—"

He strolled over to the window, pulling out a ten-dollar bill. "Thank God," he murmured, "we didn't decide to put you in charge of the campaign funds."

She took his money and tucked it into the outside pocket of her purse. "Bye, Art," she said sweetly.

"Bring me the change!" he called after her.

Then she did make a face at him, and drove off.

As soon as she was safely in the flow of traffic, she found her thoughts wandering to Trey again. Perhaps it had been Art's remark about talking to strangers which brought it all back again, but she couldn't seem to get the man out of her mind. It had been a long time since anyone had affected her this strongly on a first meeting . . . if ever. And it did not seem quite fair that he should disappear from her life as quickly as he had entered.

Lindsey was a strong believer in first impressions, but except for that brief moment last night in the restaurant—and again when he had kissed her—her first impression about this man appeared to have been entirely wrong. And perhaps that was what intrigued her most. He seemed to have two personalities: the cynical ex-prosecutor who looked for the worst and was accustomed to seeing it, and a gentler, more perceptive side, which he cautiously tried to hide from view, but which he could not completely keep from showing in his eyes. It was that part of him, the part he seemed to be guarding, which fascinated Lindsey.

Of course, it occurred to her slowly, if she really wanted to see him again, it probably wouldn't be too hard to find him. After all, there could not be too many men in Art's building with the first name Trey, and all occupants were listed on the directory. Furthermore, she remembered his office was on the seventh floor, and if she really wanted to, all she would have to do would be to—

But she would not. Firmly, she drew her thoughts back to matters at hand. She wasn't sixteen years old and she did not have time to be chasing daydreams. Her day was crowded with things to do and plans to make, and she could not waste more of it lost in a reverie involving a man she did not know and would never see again.

She delved into her household chores with enthusiasm, but in the back of her mind she was aware that he lingered. When she looked at the draperies, she remembered his hanging them; when she looked at the clutter, she was energized into organization as she wondered what he must have thought of her, seeing her apartment like that. She worked nonstop, deriving a happy satisfaction from arranging her possessions in a new place and adding original decorative touches. At

seven o'clock, just as the last light had faded irrevoca-
bly from the sky, she returned from carrying the last of
the cartons to the dumpster around the corner and she
paused to observe her handiwork.

The entire effect was one of openness and space. The
two huge windows met to frame the corner in which
she had arranged her bed, and the abstract floral print
of the draperies, in bright splashes of hot pink, pale
pink, and yellow, was the perfect frame for the pale
green of the sheer curtains and the white satin coverlet
on her bed. Near the bed was a wicker rocker piled with
colorful cushions, and a rattan nightstand. An open
wicker bookshelf divided the bedroom from the living
area, which contained two small sofas in yellow velve-
teen, a tall, deep-green chair of the same material, and
a round chrome-and-glass coffee table. An antique escritoire, which she had bought for twelve dollars at an
auction and refinished herself, led the way to the compact kitchen with its green porcelain fixtures and appli-
ances and her small, though elegant, teakwood dining
table. The white shag carpet and the use of many mir-
rors and glass-framed pictures reflected light into every
corner, and Lindsey thought delightedly, *It looks just
like a candy store!* She giggled at the comparison and
started to the kitchen to prepare dinner. All that work
had left her ravenous.

It was then that she realized she had forgotten to do
her shopping. She had also forgotten to go to the bank.
She still had the remainder of the ten dollars Art had
given her, and she supposed she had no choice but to
go out for a hamburger.

She stood there uncertainly for a moment, wondering whether to change out of the dusty and faded jeans
and the sloppy man's shirt in which she had been working, or whether to go to a drive-in where no one would
notice what she looked like. She decided she could at

least wash her face, which was streaked with dust, and then, as if on cue, the doorbell rang.

She ran to answer it, hoping Art had decided to make good on his dinner invitation sooner than planned. She flung open the door and Trey drawled, "Don't tell me you knew it was me this time."

For a moment she was speechless. She had been thinking about him all day, and now here he was, in jeans and sneakers and a casual crew-neck sweater, and it seemed entirely too unlikely to be true.

She stammered, "I—no, I—I thought you were my brother...."

He lifted an eyebrow. "Oh? Are you expecting him?"

"No," she said quickly. "That is, I—" And then she noticed the package he carried with the name of a Chinese restaurant printed on the side, and she exclaimed, drawing him inside, "Food! How did you know I hadn't had dinner?"

"Lucky guess," he replied, but she ignored the slightly dry twist to his tone as she took the package from him and inhaled the aroma delightedly.

"I meant to shop for groceries today," she explained, leading the way to the kitchen, "but I forgot to go to the bank again...." She set the package on the table and glanced at him, suddenly shy. "You're always rescuing me," she said lightly. "Usually from the brink of starvation!"

"You strike me as the type of girl who could use a lot of taking care of," he responded, and he moved to assist her as she stretched to take down the plates.

He was so near that she could feel the warmth of his body, and a curious prickling sensation started on the flesh of her arms. She started to move away, and as he lowered the plates from their top shelf his elbow brushed lightly across her breast. Lindsey jumped back as though shocked.

His eyes twinkled as he apologized blandly, "Accidents will happen." He handed the plates to her politely at an arm's distance.

Lindsey hated the color which flamed her cheeks. She was not usually so awkward with men. Her hand flew to the paisley scarf which covered her hair and then to one dusty cheek, and she exclaimed nervously, "I'm a mess!"

"But the apartment looks great," he agreed, glancing around with interest. "Do you know, if I had never been here I could have guessed this is what it would look like."

She started to the bathroom to wash her face. "Oh, yeah? How?"

"It looks like you," he explained. "Like a spring garden."

She paused at the bathroom door, her eyebrows raised in mock amazement. "Poetry? From the man who couldn't think of anything more inspired to talk about this morning than pollen?"

He grinned and shrugged. "I have my moments."

She laughed and closed the door.

She took several minutes to splash cold water on her face, brushed her hair until it positively gleamed, considered applying a little lipstick but thought that might look too obvious. She took a deep breath and went back into the kitchen, where he had already filled their plates and put the containers away. She thought she was much calmer now, in perfect control, more like herself.

But when she was seated across the table from him that prickling feeling began in her stomach again, she could feel her cheeks pinken, and she had never felt more awkward or clumsy in her life. She tried to cover it. "It smells delicious!" she exclaimed, taking up her fork. "I love Chinese food, don't you? And your timing was perfect, I—"

He looked at her quizzically. "You're chattering," he said. "Do I make you nervous?"

The question caught her off guard, but she felt no urge to dissemble. Actually, she was relieved to be able to answer a frank question directly, for she was always more at ease when dealing with people in a straightforward manner. "Yes," she admitted. "A little. I mean, I can't figure you out."

He lifted an eyebrow. "Are you supposed to?"

She laughed a little. "It helps."

"Well," he told her with a smile, "just relax. I'm a little uncomfortable with strangers myself."

His smile was so pleasant that it was impossible not to relax beneath it. She found herself wishing he would smile more often, and she challenged, teasing him, "Now, that I can't believe!"

"I'm nothing if not honest," he told her, and turned to his meal. "It's one of my worst handicaps."

"Honesty or shyness?"

"I didn't say shy," he corrected. "I said, or implied, a certain reticence with people I don't know well. A reluctance to make casual friends."

"That's the lawyer in him," murmured Lindsey to herself, her eyes twinkling. "Pedantic to a fault. What you mean to say," she told him, "is that you're so suspicious and mistrustful that it's hard for you to get close to people."

"I mean," he corrected, "I choose my friends carefully. I thought you were hungry."

She laughed and took up her fork again. Glancing at him, she inquired, "Should I be honored? Does this mean you've chosen me for a friend?"

He looked at her thoughtfully. "I'll let you know."

"You know what it is, don't you?" she replied, carefully selecting a water chestnut wrapped in tangy sauce. "You don't trust people yourself, your own judgment.

You expect the worst from people and that's exactly what you find."

That statement seemed to amuse him. "When you've lived as long as I have," he answered her, "and seen as much as I have, you'll find out exactly what I have—that half the people you meet are lying to you, and the other half using you."

Irritation flickered. She did not like the note of condescension in his tone, and she hated the cynicism. She did not like to be reminded that she, while lecturing so grandly about the value of trusting your own judgment, had vastly misjudged him. How could she ever like a man who thought like that, with whom she was forever destined to argue, who represented all the things she disliked about anyone she had ever met? And she did not like to admit that, despite all these things, she had spent most of the day thinking about him and trying to find a way to see him again, that she was unforgivably attracted to him. It was juvenile. It made her feel exactly like the child he had just implied she was.

"I wish you wouldn't refer to me as though I've just toddled out of the cradle," she snapped in annoyance. "I told you last night, I'm twenty-nine years old and I—"

"I think you're lying," he interrupted mildly.

The ember of anger flamed. The one thing she could not tolerate from anyone was dishonesty, and to be accused so blandly of being less than honest herself was utterly inexcusable. It was a silly thing, but in combination with everything else it struck a raw nerve. Her eyes flashed and she began to push away from the table. "What is your problem, anyway?" she demanded. "Just because you're dissatisfied with the human race doesn't give you the right—"

"Hey," he said gently, catching her hand. "I was teasing. Settle down."

She did so, somewhat grumpily, and played with the paper napkin in her lap. After a while, he began eating again, and she reluctantly did the same. She wished she could stay angry with him; she wished she could dislike him. She wished she could forget those few brief glimpses of the softer side of his nature and could stop being so intrigued by them. But he was constantly doing things to remind her.

"I debated all day about coming over here," he said, at last.

"So why did you?" It sounded like a disgruntled challenge, but in fact she was really curious. The answer to that question was one which had been bothering her since he had first surprised her at the door.

When she looked up, his expression was very serious, and she felt something soft and peculiarly painful spread through her chest. There it was again, the man she wanted to know, the part of him that touched her in those rare moments he let it show. She fully expected him to hide again behind some flip reply, but he surprised her by answering with studied frankness, "I had fun with you last night. I don't have fun very often."

She could not prevent a rueful smile from touching her lips. "You could have fooled me," she said.

"Besides," he added, turning back to his meal, "you remind me of someone I used to know."

Lindsey was disappointed. The worst thing that can happen to any girl is to remind a man of another woman. "Who?" she inquired, not really wanting to know.

"Myself," he answered. "Are you going to eat, or is all that food just a decoration?"

But she sank back, staring at him. "Now, you really can't expect me to let that pass! What do you mean, I remind you of yourself?"

"Myself about fifteen years ago," he said. "Full of

dreams and afflicted with tunnel vision, convinced I could change the world by simply refusing to recognize the existence of anything distasteful."

She shifted uncomfortably in her seat, disturbed. "You make me sound pretty stupid."

There was something faraway in his smile, as though he were remembering with regret something he had treasured and lost. "I don't mean to," he said.

She was touched. "So," she prompted softly, "what happened?"

He shrugged, the moment gone. "I grew up. As you will some day."

She bit back a retort, for the companionable silence in which they finished their meal was much preferable to an argument. She wished she never had to argue with him again, but she would settle for staying away from controversial subjects for the remainder of the evening.

"Do you know what this place needs?" he commented, as he helped her clear the dishes. "Plants. Lots of greenery."

She grimaced. "No way. All I have to do is look at a houseplant and it turns brown." She poured two cups of coffee and gestured him toward the sofa. "Oh, wait a minute!" she exclaimed, turning back. "We forgot the fortune cookies! You didn't throw them away did you?

He made an expression of distaste as he took his coffee from her. "You don't mean you like those things! They taste like glue."

"I know," she answered, searching through the wrappings and empty containers which littered the counter until she found the small bag which contained the cookies. "But we have to read our fortunes."

His eyes twinkled tolerantly at her. "Naturally, you believe in them."

"I believe in lots of things," she retorted.

"They're all computer print-outs, you know."

She gave him a withering look and led the way to the living area.

He sat beside her on the small sofa and watched her in patient amusement as she broke into the cookie. "'Neither a borrower or a lender be,'" she read, and then giggled. "I guess that means I had better pay my brother back the ten dollars I borrowed. Now yours," she insisted.

He placed his coffee on the table and extracted the little slip of paper from his cookie. He studied silently for such a long time that Lindsey had to demand impatiently, "Well? What does it say?"

His brows were drawn together in thought as he looked up. "I don't know." He pretended reluctance. "Is there some sort of rule that if you tell your fortune it won't come true?"

"That's just for wishes," she retorted and tried to snatch it from him.

He held the paper high over his head, affecting insult, as he placed one hand lightly on her shoulder as though to ward her off. "Just wait a minute, just a minute," he insisted. "Don't get violent." Giving her one more cautious look, he brought the paper down with an air of great importance, and said, "It says, 'Beware of freckle-faced girls with witching green eyes. They will break your heart.'"

She gave a cry of laughter and snatched for the paper. "It does not! Let me see that!"

He caught her hand to fend her off and warned, "Be careful, lady, I have a brown belt in karate."

"Naturally!" She wrestled against his hold and broke away just as he stuffed the paper into his pocket. With both hands now free, he caught her arms securely against her sides, laughter dancing boyishly in his eyes. She made one more playful attempt to free herself, only to feel his strong fingers tighten and push her farther back on the sofa. Her heart pounded with more than the exercise and her color heightened and she knew that if this went on much longer there was only one possible ending. The thought filled her with a multitude of conflicting emotions—most prominent among them being excitement and uncertainty—and to distract him, she pretended boredom with the game and inquired, "Is that good. A brown belt?"

"Good enough for you," he replied, not loosening his hold.

She pretended to think about this. "All right," she decided. "I give up."

Surprised laughter flickered in his eyes, but he drew her up to a sitting position again and released her arms. "You're not much of a challenge," he told her.

"Discretion is the better part of valor," she replied flippantly and reached for her coffee. She used both hands so that the liquid would not slosh over the rim, and she was feeling both disappointment and relief at her narrow escape. She still wasn't entirely sure why she had done it. But she slanted a glance at him as she settled back against the cushions and told him, "Anyway, my eyes are not green. They're hazel."

He left his coffee on the table, relaxing in a sideways position next to her, his arm resting on the back of the sofa just above her shoulder. "They're green," he assured her. "And don't try to argue with me. You're talking to the man who's won eight out of ten cases he's tried in the past ten years, and you haven't got a chance."

She took a sip of her cooling coffee to smother a giggle, and she said, returning her coffee to the table,

"You know, for a psychopath, you're a pretty nice guy. I mean, I've already gotten two free meals out of the deal and no end in sight."

She felt his fingers feather lightly along the back of her neck, beneath her hair, and the motion sent a light shiver down her spine. His face was very close to hers, and she was afraid to turn to look at him. All her senses seemed to be concentrated on the delicate motions of his fingers against her collarbone and her neck, and an expectant tension radiated downward into every muscle of her body. "My dear," he said softly, "you are about to receive your first lesson in Elementary Paranoia: No one is really a nice guy, and nothing in life is free."

With a gentle pressure on her neck, he guided her face to his. His lips took hers gently, slowly, and in that first moment there was an uncertainty, as though he were expecting her, or himself, to break away. But in less than a second that chance was gone. His hand slipped around her waist and her lips parted helplessly against his increased dominance. The fingers of one hand tightened against his shoulder for support while the other traveled upward from his wrist along the course of his sinewy arm and to the hard muscles of his back, and it was as though her touch electrified him. She felt his fingers tighten on her waist and his kiss became more demanding. Present reality slipped away, and she was lost in a silver-gray void, that consisted of nothing but his mouth upon hers, the tingling heat which was spreading to every part of her body, the strength of his taut muscles beneath her fingers and the need to have this moment never end.

When he moved his lips to her face, and then, with a lingering heat, to her throat, she found herself lying back on the sofa. Her breath was coming in rapid, shallow gasps, and the pounding of her heart seemed to shake the entire room. His fingers restlessly sought the softness of her breast beneath the shapeless material of her bulky shirt and cupped it gently. She knew she should stop this, it was moving too fast, but his breath was long and unsteady against her chest where her shirt opened at the neck, and it flamed against her skin. Her hands, instead of pushing him away, caressed the corded muscles of his neck and parted the silky strands of his hair and tried to urge his lips back to hers.

He kissed her lips once, softly, lingeringly, and then her eyelids and her temples. His fingers were working the buttons of her shirt with a restrained impatience, and she felt a quiver go through her as he moved away to push back the material. Her skin prickled as his fingers lightly traced a path from the hollow of her throat and then cupped her breasts and tightened about them.

"I've wanted to do this since this morning," he said softly, "when I saw you in that low-necked nightgown...." He took one nipple gently in his mouth and she moaned. "Sweet," he murmured, and his lips traveled to the other breast. "So beautiful..."

She made a sound, whether of protest or consent not even she was certain. She only knew that the ache which was building within her was unbearable, that the sensations he was creating with his tongue and his lips were ecstasy, that she had lost all reason and control of the situation, and that she was completely within the power of the sensual magic he had created. But then, something changed. He moved his face to rest against her chest, his body tensed against hers and then slowly, by fractions, began to relax. He murmured huskily, "Oh, God. What am I doing?"

Shock struck her like a pailful of cold water as he sat

up and deliberately pulled the parted material of her shirt over her breasts, working the buttons quickly and efficiently. Confusion swept through her and turned the ache inside her into bitterness as she saw the grim lines of his face, sensed the anger and tension in the taut muscles of his body, and thought that anger was directed at her. *He's going to leave me,* she thought in outrage and helplessness, *he's going to walk right out and pretend this never happened....*

But he grabbed her hand and pulled her to her feet. She was not surprised to find she was a little unsteady. "Come on," he said, propelling her toward the door. "Let's go."

"G-go?" She almost tripped over the small step which served as a foyer, and only the warm clasp of his hand about hers saved her. "Go where?"

He found her purse on the escritoire by the door and tossed it to her. She caught it clumsily as he opened the door. "For a drive," he answered, urging her through the door with a hand lightly on her back. "A nice long, cool drive."

She offered no protest as the door closed behind them and he urged her toward his car.

There they met a problem, however. Apparently there was a party going on across the street, and someone had double-parked behind Trey's green Escort. She saw his eyes go from the offending vehicle to the blazing lights of the building across the street, and she knew he had found the perfect vent for the angry frustration she had sensed just beneath the surface since his abrupt interruption of their lovemaking moments ago. She knew she did not want to deal with the scene he was about to create.

"Here," she said quickly, producing her car keys from her purse. "Take mine."

He looked at them for a moment, as though debating

whether the need to fight was stronger than the need to get away, and then, to her relief, took them with a shrug. "Why not?" he said. "I'm feeling adventurous tonight." He paused to take something out of the front seat of his car, relocked it, and guided her to her own car with a light pressure of his hand on her shoulder.

"We can't go far," she told him when they were under way. "The gas gauge is on empty and I only have eight dollars and fifty cents."

He turned toward a service station and told her, "This one's on me."

"I don't know," she murmured—and the uneasiness in her tone was only partially feigned—"that I like being indebted to you so much."

He shook his head in a gesture of rueful amusement. "You've got it wrong," he told her. His tone made her wish desperately she could see his face in the shifting shadows of the highway. "I'm the one who's getting in over my head."

But before she could question that obscure statement, he had stopped in front of the gas pumps and an attendant was approaching the window.

When Trey turned onto the freeway, he left his window down. He seemed oblivious to the chill air which was whipping back his hair and tugging at the material of his sweater, but Lindsey began to shiver. She hugged her arms and edged closer to the passenger door, trying to escape the full force of the wind. "Do you mind?" she suggested at last, pushing her hair away from her face and trying to keep her teeth from chattering. "I'm freezing!"

He glanced at her in amusement and began to roll up the window. "You cool down a lot faster than I do," he commented. "Is that the difference between the sexes, or the difference between people?"

She glared at him, wishing she could think of some

witty and very sophisticated retort, and feeling uncomfortably as though he were mocking her. She contented herself with mumbling simply, "It just means I'm not dressed for a wind tunnel, and I'm cold."

But then he turned and smiled at her, and in the dimness she saw a genuine tenderness in his eyes. She was immediately warm again.

He took her to the exclusive Paces Ferry residential area, where stately mansions and modern architectural wonders presided over immaculately landscaped gardens and artistically terraced lawns. "Oh, my," murmured Lindsey, straining her eyes to make out details in the romantic gaslight. "I've never been here before. My brother has taken me on most of the tours," she explained, "when I visited before, but this is one place I missed. Can you imagine living here? I'll bet they all have maids and butlers and two Rolls-Royces in the garage."

He chuckled. "No one has maids and butlers any more, but if you keep your eyes open you might see a Rolls or two."

Then he surprised her by turning into a driveway with two brick pillars at the entrance and lined with a high hedge, and by stopping in front of an enormous brick structure designed with two sweeping bay windows and a row of classic dormers on the second story, like a colonial plantation home. She was speechless as he turned off the engine and got out of the car.

"What—" she demanded, as he opened her door, but he simply led her up the marble-chip walk and onto the wide veranda, where he opened the door without further ado and ushered her inside.

She was impressed. She stood in the wide, parquet foyer and admired the classic lines of the spiral staircase, the miniature glass collection in a curio cabinet opposite, and the gleaming *secrétaire* which was unmistakably Queen Anne, and she murmured, "Do you *live* here?" Unconsciously, she was keeping her voice to a tone of hushed awe. "How many divorce cases did you have to settle to buy *this*?"

"I don't do divorce," he told her, and tossed the yellow envelope he had retrieved from his car onto the *secrétaire*. "I'm too sentimental." Then he called toward the staircase. "Mom! Are you home?"

Lindsey gasped, her hand flying to her throat, and stared at him. "Your mother!" In panic, she looked down at her sneakered feet, the faded jeans, the sloppy shirt. "Your *mother*! You didn't tell me we were going to meet anyone—look at me!"

Frantically, she ran a hand through her hair and then a woman's voice floated toward them, "Trey? Is that you?"

"How could you *do* this to me?" she hissed, and turned on her heel toward the door. "I'm going to wait in the car—".

He caught her arm, his eyes laughing tolerantly. "You look fine, and anyway, my mother wouldn't notice if you didn't. Besides," he added in a melodramatic undertone, drawing her forward, "it's too late now."

Lindsey turned to see a tall, elegant woman coming around the corner, and she felt herself go miserable with embarrassment. The woman was wearing a silver satin robe which exactly matched the color of her sleekly clipped hair; her eyes were enormous and just as brown as her son's, and filled with warmth and good humor.

"Well," she declared, extending her hands to him. "The prodigal returns! Give me a kiss, dear, and then introduce me to your friend."

Obediently he took her hands and kissed her cheek,

then drew Lindsey forward. She would have gladly taken that opportunity to bolt, but his grip on her arm was firm.

"Mother, this is Lindsey..." He paused there, and they both realized at once that he did not know her last name. What would his mother think of his bringing home a girl who looked as though she had just been rescued from the scrap bag and whose last name he didn't even know? She wanted to sink though the floor with embarrassment, but she broke away from his hold on her arm and stepped forward, her hand extended, supplying quickly, "Madison. Lindsey Madison."

The other woman clasped her hand warmly, smiling. "And I'm Irene MacDonald. So good to meet you, dear, though why do I get the feeling my son has made you the victim of another one of his humorless little surprises?"

Lindsey almost breathed an audible sigh of relief at the compassionate amusement in the woman's eyes, and she felt some of the scarlet fade from her cheeks. "I wasn't exactly prepared to go out," she admitted. "Trey surprises me a lot."

Irene laughed and squeezed her hand again before releasing it. "You'll get used to it," she assured her. She turned to her son. "Come on in, both of you, and have a drink. I was just wishing I had something more interesting to do than curl up with a good book, and for once, dear, your surprise is a welcome one."

She turned to lead the way out of the foyer, but Trey dropped his hand lightly on Lindsey's shoulder. "No thanks, Mom, we're not staying. I just wanted to drop off those papers you've been pestering me about. They're self-explanatory."

"And you have better things to do on a Friday night." She shot him an amused glance and found the papers where he had tossed them. "Oh, very well, then." She waved over her shoulder as she opened the envelope. "Go along and have a good time and don't give me another thought. I'll just stay here and work the night away."

Trey grinned and kissed her again. "Martyrdom doesn't suit you. I'll call you sometime."

Irene passed a very brief, though meaningful glance, to Lindsey, and responded, "You do that." Then she smiled at Lindsey and said, "It *was* lovely to meet you, dear. Will you come again when you can stay longer?"

Lindsey knew that she meant it, and she returned her smile gratefully. "Thank you. I'd like that."

"And," she added, with a slightly derogatory glance at her son, "you don't necessarily have to bring him with you."

Lindsey laughed and Trey muttered, "Ungrateful parent," and they said good night.

Lindsey sank into her seat and buried her head in her arms on the dashboard, groaning, "How could you do that to me? I've never been so embarrassed in my life!"

"You didn't like my mother?" he inquired blandly, turning the key in the ignition.

"You know that's not what I mean!" She sat up and leaned her head back against the seat, glaring at him. "She's a lot nicer than you are, if you want to know the truth! *She* would never take me to meet someone's mother when I was dressed like a street-sweeper—"

He laughed as he made the turn out of the drive. "Vanity thy name is woman!"

"Why did you do it?" she insisted. "Why did you take me there?"

"It seemed only proper," he answered casually. "Now you know for sure I'm just as respectable as you thought I was."

Her indignation faded into puzzlement, and she turned in her seat to look at him. "What do you mean?"

"Very simple," he explained. "If I were trying to be devious or underhanded, if I were a criminal or"—he glanced at her—"married, the last thing I would do is let you meet my mother. She'd be sure to spill the beans at first glance."

She laughed, conceding the logic of his thinking. "All right. So now I know you're not a criminal, and you're not married, and you come from a wealthy, respectable family..."

"Well," he interjected, "I'm not nearly as wealthy as my mother, and as for respectable.... I think my family made most of its money selling whiskey to the Indians and running guns to Mexico."

"But your mother is nice," she put in, her eyes dancing with laughter.

"She's a great old gal," he agreed negligently, his eyes on the road. "She's outlived three husbands and has her eye out for a fourth, she runs her own real estate agency and heads up half a dozen committees, and in her spare time she takes flying lessons. But," he added, "her most commendable attribute is that she keeps her nose strictly out of my business. Not bad at all, for a mother."

Beneath the flippancy she sensed an admiration and genuine affection in his tone, and she moved closer to him on the seat, a warm contentment stealing over her. Despite the embarrassment it had caused her, it gave her a cautious thrill to know he had thought enough of her to have her meet his mother.

They drove for another ten or fifteen minutes, through mostly residential areas, and Lindsey tensed as he once again turned the car into a driveway. This house was not nearly as large as the one they had left, and it was structured of gray stone, surrounded on all sides by thick deciduous trees and well-tended shrubbery, like a cottage in the woods.

"Now what?" she inquired cautiously as he got out. This house looked deserted, and only the yellow porchlight glowed against the night. He opened the door and took her hand to help her out. "Not to worry," he assured her. "No embarrassing surprises this time." He led her up the front steps and took out his keys. "This is where I live," he added, rather unnecessarily, as he unlocked the door.

As he stepped inside and turned on the entrance light, she hesitated, aware of a mixture of anxiety and anticipation tightening in her stomach. She was no novice, and after what had begun between them at her apartment, she was pretty certain in guessing why he had brought her here. Only she was not so certain how she felt about it.

He drew her in with an arm about her shoulders, announcing casually, "Home, such as it is. Make yourself comfortable; I'll get us something to drink."

Three steps led to a sunken living room; he left her at the bottom of them to turn on a lamp and then he crossed the room to the bar. It was a beautiful room, done in gleaming dark paneling and positively crowded with greenery. Every available surface held at least one potted plant, and trees and vines filled every corner. Trailing plants spilled from macramé hangers and decorated the stone mantel. One schefflera touched the ceiling and a *ficus* plant was as tall as she was. "I love it!" she exclaimed delightedly. "It reminds me of..." She looked about the room, noticing the contrast of the dark wood and the beige pit group with the lush greenery, searching for just the right image. "Of a South

American plantation. You know, like in those old movies with ceiling fans and wooden blinds—*Casablanca* and *The African Queen*."

He chuckled as he handed her her glass. "Neither of which was set in South America," he pointed out.

She shrugged. "You know what I mean." Then she looked at the drink in her hand and commented, "You didn't ask me what I wanted."

He cocked an eyebrow innocently. "It didn't occur to me. Sherry, sweet, right?"

She looked at him, her lips tightening into a smile, and agreed, "Right." And then, because she was suddenly acutely aware of his nearness, she tasted her drink and turned away from him, continuing her examination of the room.

He did not appear to notice her sudden tension. "This one," he said, directing her attention to a floor plant about three feet high with a bulbous root and a sprout of long, thin leaves, "is over twenty years old. It's an elephant's foot. They're quite rare."

She made an appreciative sound and wandered away to study the rest of the room. Bookshelves lined either side of the stairwell and went upward toward the vaulted ceiling, where the stairs opened onto a landing, which formed a sort of recessed library. That, she thought, was magnificent. On the other side of the room a tall cabinet dominated one wall, and she went to study it. Inside was his gun collection, and it contained everything from squat, cumbersome-looking muskets to sleek ivory-handled dueling pistols, and even a tiny silver-blue derringer. She knew it was quite an impressive collection from a historical viewpoint alone, but she felt compelled to murmur derisively, "That's positively disgusting. Couldn't you think of anything else to collect?"

"Like this?" He touched her arm to guide her to another glass cabinet, and there she laughed out loud in delight. It was filled with animal miniatures, some whimsical, some strikingly realistic, none more than an inch high. There were deer and squirrel; a mother duck leading a trail of ducklings hardly larger than a fingernail; a fox curled up sleeping on a log; a tiny bear cub clinging to a tree trunk; a fuzzy caterpillar inching along a twig; a chimpanzee in a T-shirt and diapers and a silly grin; kittens in a basket; and on and on, filling every shelf sometimes as many as three deep. "Why," she exclaimed, "they're adorable! They're like your mother's," she remembered.

"With a few notable differences," he agreed. "Hers are glass, mine are ceramic. She collects anything in blown glass, I limit myself to animals. And nothing in her cabinet cost under two hundred dollars; I got most of mine at a dime store. It's not a very valuable collection, but I like it."

"Oh, could I look at some of them? Touch them, I mean?"

"Sure," he agreed easily, and then she felt his hand lightly on the back of her neck. "But not now."

Her skin prickled as he lightly smoothed her hair behind one ear; she suddenly had difficulty swallowing. When she looked at him her eyes were filled with question and caution, and he met her gaze with a gentle smile. His arm dropped lightly around her shoulders as he led her toward the sofa. "If you're thinking I brought you here to take you to bed," he said softly, his hand caressing her shoulder, "you are exactly wrong."

Her eyes flew to him in surprise, and he smiled at her. "I just thought I should get that cleared up. You've been as nervous as a cat since you came in."

She took a quick sip of her drink, but still had to clear her throat before she could ask, "Why—why did you bring me here, then?"

He responded easily, "I wanted you to know how to get here, in case you ever needed a friend."

Something clenched in her throat at that simple and thoughtful sentiment, and the emotion which fluttered in her chest confused her. She tried to cover it with a light laugh. "You must be kidding! I have trouble remembering how to get from my car to my front door!"

His smile was tender. "I'll draw you a map," he promised.

They had reached the sofa; she thought they would sit down. But instead both of his hands came to hold her arms lightly, and he turned her to face him. There was a dusky light in his eyes, no further traces of humor in his expression, and his tone had dropped in timbre. Her breath quickened expectantly at his touch.

"Just so there's no misunderstanding," he said, somewhat huskily, "I suppose I should also add that it's not because you don't turn me on more than any girl I've ever known.... In fact, you've come pretty close to driving me crazy tonight...and if I tried to tell you otherwise you would know I was lying, wouldn't you?"

But he did not wait for an answer. He simply released her arms with one brief caress and went to retrieve the drink he had left on the mantel. She sank gratefully into the soft depths of the sofa, and when he returned he did not sit next to her but chose a chair a few feet away.

She sipped her drink and wrestled with the confusion and the uncertainty with which he always seemed to leave her. Nothing about him was consistent; everything was contradictory, and just when she thought she understood him, he would retreat behind that mask again and she would realize she did not know him at all. And the worst of it was that he could make her melt with a touch or quiver with a look; just by being near, he could make her yearn to hold him without ever knowing what she was really searching for.

After a moment, and beneath the relaxing influence of half a glass of wine, she found she could say easily, "You like playing games, don't you?"

"I hate it," he answered her soberly, "more than anything in the world." He placed his glass on the table and leaned toward her, his elbows on his knees, his expression perfectly open. "So let's not do it anymore, okay?"

She nodded, smiling uncertainly, hardly knowing what to say. That was all she had ever asked of anyone.

He dropped his eyes briefly and then looked at her again. "I guess we should clear the air," he said. "I don't have serious relationships with women, Lindsey—I don't have time. And I couldn't have met you at a worse time."

There was a sinking feeling somewhere in the region of her chest, and she couldn't understand why it should matter to her, on such short acquaintance, what his attitude toward relationships was. But she drew her brows together in puzzlement and asked only, "Why?"

"It's a choice," he told her, straightening up and reaching for his drink again. "Not a very pleasant one, but a choice. You see, a relationship requires commitment, even if it's only to yourself. And I can't afford to make that kind of commitment right now. I have too many other priorities. And of course the frightening thing about you is that you're not the type of girl a man easily forgets," he added with a small, rather wry smile, lifting his glass to her.

She returned his smile. "Is that so bad?"

"Probably. I don't have a lot of room in my life for"—he seemed to hesitate over the word—"involvements."

She said carefully, watching him, "I see."

She finished her drink and set the glass on the table, knowing perfectly well that he did not mean that as harshly as it had sounded. "Well," she declared, smoothing her hands on her jeans in preparation for standing, "now that I've been properly brushed off..."

"Is that what you are?" he asked, an amused light in his eyes. "Sit down. I've got the car keys, remember?"

She settled back, somewhat disgruntled, and demanded, "And what if I told you that I don't get involved either? That all I look for in a relationship with a man is a few good times and no hard feelings on either side?"

"Then you would be lying," he answered easily. "And," he went on smoothly, before she could interrupt, "since you don't lie, you would never say such a ridiculous thing. I know this though," he added, and his brown eyes were as frank and as casual as though he were discussing the weather. "You don't get involved with anyone you've known less than two days. Which is just as well, because I'm pretty tired of ending relationships with the rather disappointing discovery that we never had any more in common than that we were good in bed." He smiled at her. "Now, I'd say I've done my part to put an end to game-playing. What about you?"

Lindsey was a little taken aback. She had never had a discussion quite this serious or quite this blunt with a man before. She felt a pinkish color tinge her cheeks, and she avoided his eyes. "I haven't had a lot of relationships," she admitted. "They've all been disappointing, I guess, and I never was really very interested. I had so many other things to do with my life." *Until now,* she thought, and kept her eyes averted because she did not want him to read what was written there.

"Which is a delicate way of saying that you don't sleep around," he said easily, and when her eyes flew to his face there was no mockery there, only a patient understanding. "I knew that."

She smiled at him gratefully, and he returned it in a moment of tenderness that was pure and honest; it warmed Lindsey to the very depths of her being. Then he stood abruptly, extending his hand to her. "Come on, I'd better take you home. It's getting late, and all this talk and no action is making me restless."

She laughed and placed her hand in his.

THE CAR DID NOT START on the second try, or the third, and by the fourth, to Lindsey's horror, the battery began to grind down to a pitiful whining sound. Trey said nothing for a time, folding his hands across the steering wheel and staring straight ahead. She thought he was fighting back temper, and she bit her lip and offered no enjoinder.

At last he said, very quietly, "I take it you didn't make it to the garage."

"I—I forgot."

Another long silence. Then, very softly, "Lindsey, damn it all..." His voice sounded peculiar, and when she glanced at him she was amazed to see his shoulders shaking in silent laughter. "I don't know whether to hit you or kiss you." He looked at her, his eyes dancing madly. "Looks like you're staying the night."

As he helped her out of the car once again she insisted quickly, "I could call a cab. It's not far and—"

"For a girl with only eight-fifty to her name," he interrupted, ushering her without ceremony up the stairs, "you're pretty free with your money. Besides, that would still leave me without a car and it's too late to worry about it tonight." He opened the door on a small room, obviously not the master bedroom, and told her, the twinkle still dancing in his eye despite the serious expression, "Fortunately for you, I'm known for my strength of character."

The room contained one chest of drawers, a desk with a clock radio, and an unmade bed.

"I don't believe anyone has slept here since I moved in," he said. "I hope it will be comfortable. If you want to take a shower, the bathroom's across the hall, and there's a robe hanging on the back of the door you can use."

"Thanks, I do feel kind of grimy." She smoothed a pillow and straightened up, smiling at him uncertainly.

He nodded, and glanced about the room, adding, "The extra blankets are in the closet, if you get chilly, or"—he turned to her with an inviting grin—"my room is right next door."

"Why, sir," she protested, feigning insult, "I'm shocked." And he laughed.

"I'm only human, Lindsey." He stepped forward and took her in his arms, his expression sobering as he added, "So lock your door." He bent and kissed her lips once very lightly, and then again, almost a feather touch. "Good night, Lindsey," he whispered, and turned to go.

She smiled and closed the door after him. But she did not lock it.

Chapter Five

It was a strange feeling, to awake nude beneath the covers of a bed which was not her own—strange, but not unpleasant, for with it clung the drowsy scraps of a delightful dream. She had dreamed Trey was making love to her, and she huddled deep into the pillows, trying to recapture the ephemeral sensations and rosy colors which were too soon slipping away. Gradually, she realized it had been only a dream; gradually, she remembered where she was and how she came to be here; and stretching luxuriously, she lay there for a moment longer, looking forward to the adventure this day would hold.

The morning air was chilly on her bare arms, and she reached for the robe she had worn after her shower the night before. The dark blue velour was soft against her skin, and a hint of his lime cologne clung to the folds, reminding her of how it had felt to be held in his arms, reminding her of all the excitement and conflict and unexpected happiness of the day before, and reminding her that the day ahead looked just as promising.

She simply wrapped the robe about her as she hurried across the room to the chair on which she had left her clothes, and she pulled on the old jeans and baggy workshirt quickly against the chill air. She took a comb from her purse and made a quick stop at the bathroom to wash her face and straighten her hair, then made her way toward the stairs.

The aroma of coffee and bacon led her to the kitchen, where Trey was working at a copper-tone stove. The kitchen itself was something of a surprise; it was larger than she would have expected, done in dark wooden crossbeams and white stucco, reminding her of something from a gourmet cooking magazine. Copper pots gleamed in the bright fluorescents over a center work island, and a myriad of complicated-looking utensils were displayed on a corkboard wall. Small green plants in clay pots nestled in the space between the rafters and the ceiling. There were two built-in ovens and a microwave, a six-burner range, double-wide refrigerator, and every modern appliance for food preparation known to man. She simply stood there for a moment, looking around her in awe.

"Your timing is rotten," Trey greeted her. "Another two minutes and I would have had the pleasure of serving you breakfast in bed."

She grinned and came into the room. "The story of my life. A day late and a dollar short." She slid onto one of the stools at the bar which divided the kitchen lengthwise and added, "This kitchen is fantastic. You must be a gourmet cook."

Trey was dressed this morning in jeans which were as battered and faded as her own, paint-splattered, and tight enough to outline the taught shape of his thighs and emphasize the firm flatness of his abdomen. In the casual dark T-shirt and sandals he looked relaxed and perfectly at home as he placed before her a plate of eggs, crisp bacon, and butter-soaked wedges of toast. He shrugged and answered, "I like to fool around in the kitchen. I leave most of the real cooking to professionals, though."

"You do a lot of entertaining?"

He brought his own plate and sat across from her, pouring two glasses of orange juice. "Part of the job."

She took a bite of her eggs, made an appreciative sound of delight, and exclaimed, "These are terrific!"

"Romano cheese and just a hint of sour cream," he informed her, taking up a wedge of toast. His expression was bland. "I'm glad you appreciate my culinary talents; now you won't mind so much doing the dishes."

"Ha!" She turned back to her meal with enthusiasm. "The only thing I do worse than cook is wash dishes."

His eyes twinkled. "It's never too late to learn."

She made a face at him and lifted a large forkful of eggs.

When they sat sipping coffee, she inquired, somewhat reluctantly, "Have you figured out a way to get me home yet?"

He lifted one beautifully shaped eyebrow in mock surprise. "Tired of me already? I thought after I seduced you with one of my meals you would be mine forever."

"I don't come that cheap," she told him archly.

"Still, it's pretty easy to see the way to your heart is through your stomach."

"Gluttony is only one of my faults," she admitted, hiding a smile behind the rim of her cup. "And anyway, what would you do with my heart if you had it?"

"Break it, probably," he responded lightly, and rose, catching her hand to draw her around the bar to him. "But first, we have business to take care of. I'm going to get your car started and drive to the parts store, and then replace everything under that hood except the engine. And you," he informed her, touching her nose lightly, "are going to help me. But first"— he glanced meaningfully at the pile of pots and pans and used plates in the sink—"wash the dishes."

She stuck out her tongue at him and started to pull

away, but his eyes snapped suddenly in acknowledgment of her unintentional invitation, and he drew her to him, covering her open mouth swiftly with his own. She was taken by surprise, and her heart lurched and her breath caught at the warm, unexpected sensation of his tongue exploring the recesses of her mouth, flicking over her teeth, teasing her tongue. Her one hand was still caught in his, and she felt the slow tightening of his fingers on hers, the increased heat; his other hand pressing lightly on her back and the contact of their mouths were all that held them together, but she could feel tension from each of his muscles even as her own went weak, and she had to bring her hand to his waist for support.

He released her slowly, leaving for a moment only the hot fan of his breath on her cheek and the taste of him on her lips. His hand closed over her hand on his waist and removed it; he took one step backward, holding her hands, his eyes fastened upon hers with a slow, hungry light, his smile vague.

"I can see right now there's no time to waste in getting you home where you belong," he said softly. "Any woman who can make me think the crazy things you do at eight o'clock in the morning is more than a little dangerous."

When he left her she went quickly to the sink and busied herself with the dishes, thinking he was probably right—the sooner she was home, the better. Every time he touched her, his power over her increased, and this entire relationship was progressing much too fast. She had only known him two days, and if the truth be told, she still really knew nothing about him except that he was cynical and pessimistic, ultraconservative, and basically not the sort of person she should have gotten along with at all. And that he collected whimsical animal miniatures and had a passion for growing things and an unexpected talent for cooking, and that when he laughed she was transported into a magical world that made her feel warm and contented utterly right... and that he did not get involved. Yes, all things considered, it would be much safer if she were to return home as quickly as possible and give this thing which was developing between them a chance to cool off.

The only trouble was, Lindsey was not accustomed to playing it safe.

Trey's front lawn was artistically landscaped and terraced with heavy timbers to form planting beds for flowering shrubs and trees. The drive was lined with a series of cedarlike shrubs about five feet high which looked like miniature Christmas trees, and the view from the street was blocked by a row of silver maples. A huge magnolia tree shaded the entire front of the house, and spaced strategically about the wide lawn were shapely cedars and white-barked crepe myrtles. Honeysuckle bloomed riotously along a high wooden side fence, spilling its cloying scent into the air to mingle wantonly with that of early blooming primroses and fresh spring grass. If there were neighbors on either side Lindsey did not see or hear them, and while appreciating the beauty and the quiet, she had to comment, "You like your privacy, don't you?"

He glanced up from the intricate maneuvers he was making beneath the hood of the car and followed her gaze around the yard. "Oh, you mean all the trees? It's more of a necessity than a choice, I guess. Hand me that crescent wrench, will you?"

Lindsey was sitting cross-legged on the drive with a handful of tools. Having no idea what a crescent wrench was, she presented the entire collection to him; he chose the one he needed. "Okay," she said, "if you weren't a burglar before you were a lawyer, you were an auto mechanic, right?"

"Wrong."

"What were you, then?"

He grinned at her. "A spoiled rich kid. Come up here and let me show you what I'm doing. If you learn to do these things for yourself, you won't always be at the mercy of others."

"I've never felt like I was at the mercy of anyone," she replied with a slight frown as she got to her feet.

"You are," he told her, "a babe in the woods. A case in point: If I were less than scrupulous, I could decide to just let your car sit there. I could lock you upstairs and take away your clothes and no one would ever hear from you again."

"You wouldn't do that," she retorted, despite the fact that a blush was tingling her cheeks at the image he had presented. "Your car is being held hostage at my apartment, remember?"

"In fantasies," he told her, intent upon the work he was doing, "details like that don't matter."

She laughed, pretending amazement. "What? Fantasies from the hard-headed realist? I don't believe it."

The gleam in his eye was wicked as he glanced at her. "I've discovered a whole new repertoire since last night. Want to hear some more?"

Because he looked just devilish enough to enjoy doing it, she backed away from the offer. She cleared her throat a little uncomfortably, relaxed her face into studious lines, and discovered a sudden interest in automobile repair. "Tell me what you're doing now," she suggested, focusing her attention on the mechanical jungle beneath the hood of her car, and he laughed.

The job promised to take all day, and Lindsey's feigned interest soon developed into a real one. Being with him, watching him work, asking him hundreds of questions which he patiently answered, reminded her of childhood days with her father, and as they stopped at noon to have sandwiches and lemonade on the back patio, she told him so.

"You remind me of him," she said, "in a lot of ways."

"That's transparently Freudian, my dear," he drawled lazily. His dark eyes were squinted against the sun and glinting with flecks of gold. Sprawled out in the lounge chair, the skin of his arms and his neck gleaming with a light film of perspiration and his wind-ruffled hair sparkling copper in patches where the sun struck it, he sipped his lemonade and looked relaxed and completely at peace with the world. Lindsey felt a rush of affection for him and a sudden sense of camaraderie which was completely inexplicable and all the more wonderful because it was so.

She shrugged. "Maybe, but it's true. My father was good with his hands, too. There was nothing he couldn't fix or make, and he was always busy. He especially liked small things and intricate work. He was an intellectual, too, but," she added slyly, "mostly he was a dreamer. Just like you."

For a moment the glance he shot her was startled, just as it had been the last time she had surprised him by uncovering a truth about himself he had thought to have kept well hidden. But almost immediately it relaxed into amusement, and he replied, "I'm neither an intellectual nor a dreamer. I'm a pragmatist. And you're looking much too hard for things which aren't there."

"Oh, I don't think so," she responded casually, leaning back in her chair and letting her eyes wander toward a trellised rose garden which was not yet in bloom. "I think you're trying much too hard to hide things which are there—possibly even from yourself. And you see," she added lightly, "it was your fate to meet me, so that I could remind you of all those noble things you've forgotten about yourself."

He chuckled and turned his face back to the sun, closing his eyes. "I don't believe in fate."

"You don't believe in anything," she retorted.

He shrugged. "Oh, I used to believe in a lot of things. Truth, justice, the basic goodness of the human race...along with Santa Claus and the tooth fairy and other assorted nonsense."

She stirred uncomfortably, frowning. "Just when I think I'm starting to like you, you come out with something like that. I think you do it just to try to make me argue."

He turned to look at her, grinning. "Could be. If you had any idea how stimulating you look when defending some high-flown and perfectly worthless principle, you wouldn't blame me much." He turned away and closed his eyes again, adding, "Take my advice and don't let yourself be fooled into liking me too much. I'm a professional charmer."

She remembered their first encounter on the elevator, his stiffness and disagreeability afterward, the many times he had appeared to go out of his way to make her angry, and she burst into laughter. "Don't worry. You're not in any danger of winning a congeniality award as far as I can tell."

"That's because I'm on a vacation," he murmured drowsily.

"From the charm business?" she teased.

"From life in general, maybe." He opened his eyes a crack and slanted them at her. "I have a feeling you have that basic effect on people—total escapism. The Tahiti syndrome. It's because you see life through rose-colored glasses and you make everyone else want to see it that way too. It's a dangerous practice, Lindsey. I speak from experience, and I don't recommend it."

Seriousness had crept into his tone during the last part of his speech, and it made her uncomfortable. The day was so lovely and she was enjoying his company so much that she refused to spoil it with a disagreeable conversation. She stood decisively. "I won't be able to escape to anywhere, much less Tahiti, if you don't put my car back together. Let's get back to work."

The afternoon sun grew warm, and perspiration mixed with the streaks of oil and grime on Trey's face. Lindsey cuffed up her jeans and kicked off her shoes and tried to push up the sleeves of the oversized flannel shirt, but they kept falling down. Trey commented, "You must be smothering in that thing. Why don't you go inside and change?"

"Into what?" she retorted, pushing back her damp hair with an oily hand which left a black streak across her forehead.

"You'll find a T-shirt in the top drawer of my dresser," he told her. "It may not be the latest thing in designer fashions, but it will be a lot cooler."

She looked down at her crumpled shirt and jeans and replied dryly, "Do I look like a girl who's particularly interested in designer fashions?" Then she glanced at him shrewdly. "I can't believe you actually let strangers rummage through your personal belongings. For all you know, I could be a thief or a spy..."

He grinned. "For the price of a T-shirt, I'll take the chance."

"Why, you reckless devil," she murmured and then scrambled toward the house as he threw an oil-stained rag at her.

The white T-shirt was several sizes too large, but still it did nothing to hide her unmistakable feminine curves. She was not wearing a bra, and she felt utterly naked before Trey's slow, appreciative grin. "It's much cooler," she told him negligently, fighting back a blush, and resumed her position as keeper of the tools. He chuckled and restrained himself from comment.

The sun was beginning to set when he closed the hood and wiped his hands with satisfaction on one of the grimy workcloths. "You couldn't get a better job at twice the price," he declared in satisfaction, and crossed the lawn to hook up a garden hose to the faucet. "Now all it needs is a good bath."

Lindsey examined her oil-blackened hands and arms and agreed, "I could use one too."

"Is that right?"

Without warning, he turned the full spray of the garden hose on her. She squealed and sputtered and tried to defend herself with her hands against the stream of cold water, and in a matter of seconds she was drenched from head to toe. She stumbled toward him, gasping angrily, and wrenched the nozzle from him as he laughed mercilessly. In another moment his laughter became startled as she turned the hose on him; he wrestled it from her and tossed it aside as she demanded, dripping, "What did you do that for? Look at me, I'm soaked, it wasn't a bit funny—"

Water dripped from his hair into his madly dancing eyes as he caught her shoulders and replied, "Did you really think I could resist the temptation to see you in a wet T-shirt?"

Her sputtering accusations were smothered in his mouth. One arm slipped around her waist, his fingers firmly molding the soft flesh beneath the thin layer of wet material, and his other arm slipped about her shoulders, cradling her head in the crook of his elbow. Their faces, at first cold from the drenching, quickly flamed to heat, her breasts were crushed against the hardness of his chest and the pounding of his heart became intermingled with her own. She longed to let her arms travel upward, to trace the breadth of his back and wind themselves about his neck, but he was holding her so tightly she could not move. She contented herself with resting her hands lightly on his hips, her fingers curled into his front pockets.

Slowly, reluctantly, his embrace loosened, his hand traveled downward to caress and then to firmly cup her rounded bottom, pressing her against his strong length for one last moment of deepening passion before his lips left hers. He slid his hand about her neck and pressed his lips tenderly to her cheek, and then to her forehead, and then, drawing her head to his chest, he simply rested his chin lightly atop her hair, holding her.

She thought nothing could be more wonderful than to be held like this by him forever, and too weak to move, she rested against him, hearing nothing but the slow, steady rhythm of his heart against her ear and the unsteady whisper of her own breath, feeling nothing but the warm glow of ecstasy his embrace had left. After a long time he took a small step backward, looping his arms about her waist, and smiled down at her tenderly. "You wouldn't believe," he said softly, "where you have greasy handprints."

She dropped her eyes demurely. She was still holding on to his pockets for support, and for the first time she realized that her fingers had closed about a small slip of paper inside one of them. "What is this?" she inquired, starting to draw it out.

His eyes crinkled. "Don't be naive."

She fought a blush and waved the paper in front of him. "I mean," she told him, "this." And then she exclaimed, "Why, it's your fortune from last night!"

He lifted his shoulders lightly. "I guess it is. I found it lying around this morning."

She started to unfold it but then glanced at him. "Do you mind if I read it now?"

His smile was complacent. "I'm not sure I trust you

enough." But he made no objection as she read the message silently to herself: " *'Tis better to have loved and lost than never to have loved at all."*

She tilted her head toward him, smiling, and inquired, "Appropriate?"

"You're the fortune-teller; you tell me."

She dropped her eyes to study the paper, pretending thoughtfulness. "I think," she decided finally, glancing up at him, her eyes twinkling, "I'm hungry."

He laughed and draped his arm about her shoulder, squeezing it briefly as they started toward the house. "I should have guessed. Just give me a minute to shower and change, and then I'm going to fix you the most unforgettable steak dinner you've ever had in your life."

LATER, they sat across the candlelit table sipping wine, sharing the silence. Lindsey had changed back into her old shirt, but in the candlelight her inappropriate attire melted into the shadows, her hair formed a soft halo about her face, and her eyes glowed softly. Trey was watching her with an absent, thoughtful expression on his face, and at last Lindsey broke the silence by inquiring softly, "What are you thinking about?"

He smiled vaguely, lifting his glass. "I wish you hadn't asked me that."

"Why?"

"Because now I have to tell you the truth."

She leaned back and sipped her wine, pushing back a small sense of trepidation, wondering if there were anything he could possibly say to surprise her. This was the man who believed in nothing, but treasured a scrap of paper from a fortune cookie; who trusted no one, but went out of his way to rescue a lady in distress; who constantly amazed her with hard cynicism one moment and unexpected tenderness the next. The man with the lines of a warrior carved into his face and the look of a dreamer in his eyes. She had learned to be prepared for anything. "Go ahead," she assured him. "I can take it."

He replaced his glass on the table, his hands looped loosely about the stem, his eyes dark and studious as they examined hers. "I'm thinking what beautiful hands you have, so white and delicate—even with grease under the fingernails."

She clenched her hands automatically, and he laughed. "Unfair," she accused. "I thought you were going to tell the truth."

"All right." He sat back, and the twinkle in his eye slowly faded to something more serious. "I was wondering what it is about you that makes me feel I've known you forever. I was wishing I had never gotten on that elevator Thursday night, because I think I've gotten myself into a hell of a mess."

Now she was surprised. Her eyes widened and her breath caught, and in a moment she managed, "I—I don't understand. Why?"

He dropped his eyes briefly. "It's been a long time since I met a woman I wanted to see more than once. You wouldn't believe how long. It's been a long time since I've enjoyed myself with anyone as much as I have with you these last two days, and I'm not sure I like the feeling. I told you before, I don't have time for involvements."

"So who's asking you to get involved?" she retorted flippantly, taking another long sip of her wine. Her stomach felt tight and it was hard to swallow, and she wasn't certain exactly what he was trying to say. She only knew she hoped it was not good-bye.

"You are," he told her seriously, "whether you realize it or not. You've complicated my life more in the past forty-eight hours than you would believe."

She wondered if he had any idea he had done the same to hers. Less than a week ago all she had cared about was winning an election and doing her job. The only person who had mattered in her life was Addison Cantrell. If she were sensible, she would admit she had no time for involvements, either. Only she thought it was a little too late to worry about becoming involved, and she was hardly ever sensible.

She dropped her eyes to shield these reflections, and then looked up at him with a smile. "You have very poetic eyes," she told him.

He acknowledged her signal to move the subject on to lighter topics with a relaxed smile of his own. "Can't help it," he replied. "I was born that way. Like you and your freckles."

She groaned and brought her hands up to cover her cheeks and the bridge of her nose. "Don't mention freckles in my presence if you value my friendship. I hate them."

He reached across the table to pull her fingers away from her face, and the light in his eyes was tender. "Well, I value your friendship," he said, "but I also like your freckles. I'll mention them as often as I like."

The moment was threatening to evolve into one filled with more emotion than she really felt she could handle just then, and she slowly withdrew her hands, rested her chin upon them and inquired innocently, "Am I being privileged to witness your famous professional charm?"

His eyes twinkled as he sat back and replied, "When I decide to turn on the charm, believe me, you'll know it. Right now," he added, rising, "I think the best thing to do is to take you home before I'm tempted to charm you into spending another night."

"What makes you think you could?" she retorted, accepting his extended hand as she got up from the table.

"Two things," he responded confidently. "First, I can be absolutely irresistible when I want to be. And second"—he winked at her—"I still have the keys to your car."

She laughed and leaned her head against his shoulder as he guided her to the door.

She was surprised that the drive from Trey's house to hers took less than fifteen minutes. "Think you can find your way back?" Trey inquired.

She shook her head at the maze of twists and turns, shortcuts and back roads he was taking. "No chance," she replied decisively.

He glanced at her. His face, in the sudden flash of passing headlights, was amused. "Did it ever occur to you that you're something of an anachronism in this day and age? Helpless female in the nineteen-eighties—it's absurd. You should be preserved in glass."

She bristled. "I assure you I am far from helpless," she replied coldly. "And being female has nothing to do with it." She wondered where all the good humor and easy companionship of the day had gone. She wondered again whether he did it on purpose, knowing exactly what kind of comments would annoy her, trying to goad her into another display of righteous indignation. She restrained herself as best she could. "If you think remarks like that are cute," she added, "they're not. And if you're trying to make me feel ridiculous, don't bother. Better men than you have tried."

"Yes," he agreed easily, "I imagine you get a lot of teasing. That's because there's something irresistibly endearing about an absentminded, accident-prone, perpetually disorganized female. Why do you think dumb blondes are so popular? They make a man feel superior and protective . . . and unthreatened."

"Well, I am *not* a dumb blonde," she retorted archly, "or a dizzy redhead, either, for that matter, and I don't particularly like being treated like one." *Especially not by you,* she thought, but did not say, and she was not certain why she should suddenly feel so defensive about certain personality defects she had long since learned to accept in herself. She suspected she resented the fact that he was being intentionally abrasive more than any particular thing he had said.

"Then I apologize. I was not trying to be cute or to make you feel ridiculous. As a matter of fact"—he glanced at her casually—"as you might have guessed, I rather like you, and if I sometimes make you angry with my lectures or my teasing try to remember I'm only doing it for your own good."

The cautious expectation which had risen at his first words was lost in the patronizing tone of his last, and her spirits fell. "I know, I know," she replied sarcastically. "Poor little innocent Lindsey, so simple, so trusting, so desperately in need of looking after—no one wants to see her hurt."

"No," he responded seriously, "getting hurt is part of life. I wouldn't try to deprive you of that experience. I would only want you to be prepared, and when your ideals are crushed and your dreams are gone and you start to see the world for the cold, hard place it is—I would want you to know that you'll survive. You'll pick yourself up and start again, older, wiser, and all the better for it, just like the rest of us did."

She looked at him, touched by the beauty and the perception of his speech, the sensitive philosophy behind it. She did not know what to say. In his words and in the soft, reflective quality of his voice he had shared a part of himself which she suspected few were ever privileged to see. She felt honored, and deeply moved, and closer to him than she had ever felt to anyone.

He parked the car in front of her building, and as he walked around to open her door the quality of his mood changed. It was not the remote mask she had grown used to seeing at first—she felt confident she would never see that one again—but the light casualness which had characterized most of their last two days together. He pressed her keys into her hand with a grin and said, "Thanks for the ride, kid. Let's do it again some time."

"A gentleman," she retorted, slipping her arm through his, "would walk me to my door."

"And as we both know," he agreed soberly, "I'm a perfect gentleman."

He unlocked her door, turned on the light, and returned her keys. Still on the threshold, he took her shoulders and said, "Now allow the perfect gentleman to say a gentlemanly goodnight."

She looked up at him in confusion. "Aren't you coming in?"

He shook his head slowly, a small, regretful smile on his lips. "No," he said softly. "If I did that, I'm afraid we would end up in bed, and if we did that, I'm very much afraid I wouldn't be able to let you go in the morning... or the morning after that, or the morning after that. So ..." He bent his head toward her, his eyes deep with a soft, inner light, his lips full and parted and whispering on hers, "Good night ..."

Eagerly, her hands clasped about his neck, her lips parted beneath his swift demand, and the passion which flamed and swept her was just as intense, just as unexpected, as it had been the first time they kissed; it left her dizzy. When he moved his lips to her face she clung to him, holding on to his open collar against a mindless weakness. His breath was hot against her ear and she shivered.

His hands tightened on her arms, the strong pressure of his fingers against her soft flesh sending a new cascade of anticipation through her. He seemed undecided whether to draw her closer or push her away. "I'll call you tomorrow," he whispered.

She nodded. Far away a door slammed, and she became aware of the high, musical chirping of crickets. She whispered, "I—I don't remember my number."

She felt, rather than saw, him smile. He dropped his lips swiftly to her hair. "Figures."

She felt his muscles tense in preparation for moving away. She made herself release her hold on his collar, she strengthened herself for standing alone. She tried very hard to remind herself that she had known him only two days and that neither of them was ready for an involvement. She knew that they were already more involved than either of them had intended, and that if she asked him to stay, he would... and that she would never be satisfied with a one-night stand. But she could not completely sever the contact between them so abruptly. She touched his arm lightly. "Trey..."

He turned. She searched his face anxiously in the dark, not certain exactly what she was looking for. More than anything, she wanted to ask him to stay. But she suddenly became aware of the cold concrete against her bare feet and she heard herself saying, "I—I forgot my shoes."

For a moment there was absolute silence. Then he began to chuckle softly; he brought her fingers to his lips and kissed them swiftly, shaking with suppressed mirth. "Good night, Lindsey," he said, and he turned and went down the walk, still laughing.

Chapter Six

The next morning Lindsey was awakened by a sudden glare of brilliant light. She moaned and rolled over, squinting and shielding her eyes, and then she gasped and sat up straight. Standing over her, outlined in the brilliance of the morning sun, was the figure of a man, and a stern voice accused her, "You left your door unlocked again."

She drew the sheet up to her chin, blocking out some of the light with a hand before her face, and gradually she made out formidable, familiar features. "Trey?"

"When are you going to learn this is *not* Cedar Falls?" He came toward her, moving out of the glare of the light, and she could see him more clearly. He was dressed in jeans; a knit shirt and a navy poplin Windbreaker completed the casual, yet well-dressed look. Sunday morning in the city, thought Lindsey drowsily, and was relieved to notice his face did not reflect the anger his voice had carried. "What would you do right now if it was someone other than myself standing here?" he demanded.

"Turn over and go back to sleep," she responded, yawning. "What are you doing here, anyway?"

"Trying to get it through your thick head that it would be just as easy for a criminal to walk in here while you were sleeping as it was for me," he answered shortly. "I'm not asking much, Lindsey, just a little common sense—"

"Well, that's the difference between you and me," she said, smothering another yawn with both hands. "You're always worrying about protecting yourself against the bad guys; I think of locked doors in terms of all the good things they keep out."

He sat beside her on the bed, a slow, mischievous smile tugging at the corners of his lips. "Is that right?" he questioned, pulling at the sheet which hugged her chest.

She snatched the sheet away from him, the awareness of his touch propelling her into immediate and delightful alertness. The full impact of the happiness which had crept through her upon awakening to find him there swept away the last traces of sleepiness and galvanized her for another day brimming with promise.

She tried unsuccessfully to look stern as she demanded, "What are you doing here at this hour of the morning? Don't you know it's un-American to get up at sunrise on Sunday? There ought to be a law."

"I came," he informed her, leaning back with his hands supporting his weight on the bed, "to return your shoes. And I'll have you know that the sun has been up for almost four hours, and the passage of any such law to the contrary is, I'm afraid, beyond my power."

She could fight back a smile no longer, even as she grumbled, "It's indecent."

"Only fitting," he replied. His eyes flickered over the unmistakable shape of her body beneath the sheet, and unconciously, she inched farther back against the headboard, tightening her hold on the flowery material of the bedclothes and moving her leg away from the warm brush of his thigh. "As it happens, I've been kept awake most of the night by thoughts which were, for the most part, very indecent."

She replied with a cautious "Oh?" and was not at all sure she could handle this at this hour of the morning. The warm languor of sleep still hampered her thought processes and muted warnings of danger, and he was much too close. It would be so easy to open her arms and draw him next to her on the bed, and her emotions were a mixture of excitement and trepidation.

"Yes," he answered. His tone was matter-of-fact, and his eyes reflected nothing but a faint, curious interest in the topic at hand. "I was wondering what it is between us. You know what I mean—the thing that makes me forget I'm a rational man whenever I touch you. It's more than just a natural sexual attraction. I've never known anything like it."

She gave a nervous little laugh of surprise and her hands tightened on the sheet. She had never known a man like him either, and it was more than the undeniable physical reaction he could provoke in her with a brush of his fingers or a simple glance. He carried bluntness and honesty to a point not even she was capable of doing, and the last thing she would have expected was a dispassionate discussion of their mutual sexual attraction while he sat beside her on the bed in the bright light of a Sunday morning.

"Do you always have to have a rational explanation for everything?" she demanded lightly, trying to find a way to distract him from what could be a very dangerous line of conversation.

He sat up lazily. "Of course. It's the mark of civilization."

He bent over her, his hand lightly brushed through the thick copper and mahogany fall of hair across her forehead. Her breath quickened, and his eyes were enormous and infinite, filling all of her vision. "Is it just body chemistry," he suggested softly, his fingers lightly tracing the planes of her face, "or something in the air? Maybe it's your perfume, or the way your nose crinkles when you laugh, or all those freckles you hate so much." One finger paused to touch her nose, and his lips dropped lightly and briefly to hers. "Maybe it's the way you taste." His eyelids dropped slowly, and with exquisite control and maddening slowness, his lips closed upon hers again.

She was lost in the sweetness of his kiss, the gentle way his lips moved upon hers, as though exploring and savoring a great treasure. His skin was soft and warm against hers, and the bright morning fragmented beneath her closed eyes into thousands of dancing golden sunbeams. Her arms crept about his neck, her fingers separated the thick strands of his hair, and the sheet fell away unheeded. His hand traveled slowly upward to cup her left breast, his thumb gently caressing her nipple beneath the light material of her cotton nightshirt to an aching tautness; she moaned softly, tightening her arms about him.

He moved his face to rest against hers on the pillow, his hand to lie against the delicate pattern of her ribs. For a long time he said nothing, and they simply held one another. Lindsey thought she could ask little more from life than that that moment go on forever.

And then he lifted himself a little to look at her. The smile in his eyes was tender. "And maybe," he said softly, lightly caressing her cheek with one finger, "it's because you wear your innocence like a protective umbrella, and when I'm with you I feel nothing bad can happen to me."

A thrill of happiness went through her, it shone in

her eyes as she tightened her arms about him. "Oh, Trey," she sighed, "do you have to analyze everything? Can't you just accept things and go with them?"

"No," he said seriously, holding her hands as he sat up. "I can't take chances like that. I have to understand everything very clearly, examine every situation from every angle—call it a quirk. You see," he explained—and the expression in his eyes was the most sober she had ever seen there; she had a feeling he was trying to tell her something with those eyes he was not yet ready to put into words—"I don't make promises or commitments very often, but when I do, I keep them. Forever. So I have to be very careful."

Her lips parted on a question, her eyes searched his anxiously for the real meaning behind his words, and then, abruptly, his mood changed.

He jerked back the covers and commanded severely, "Get out of that bed, woman, and get some clothes on while you still have a chance."

She laughed, startled, and wrestled for the sheet, and his eyes fell on the line of her smooth white thighs which the red-and-white nightshirt did not quite cover.

"I wish I hadn't done that," he murmured.

His hand came forward, but instead of caressing, he slapped her leg playfully and repeated, "Get dressed. We've got things to do."

She scrambled out of bed and out of his reach, demanding, "Like what?"

The short nightshirt hugged her hips and the soft swell of her breasts, and his eyes followed her across the room with an appreciative light. She slipped quickly into the terry robe she had tossed on a chair the night before. "I don't know," he answered her question. "But I've canceled a golf date that's likely to cost me as much as two thousand dollars, so it had better be good."

She arched her eyebrows in surprise. "Two thousand dollars? You must bet on yourself pretty heavily."

He feigned insult. "A perfect saint such as myself *never* gambles." He leaned back on his elbows, watching her take her clothes from the closet. "I was referring to the fact that more business deals are consummated on the golf course than in the boardroom. Sailing," he decided suddenly, just as she pulled a pair of cream-colored slacks and a flowery silk blouse from the closet. "We'll go sailing."

She returned that outfit and chose instead a pair of poplin knickers, a white polo shirt, and a bright red jacket. He grinned when she came out of the bathroom. "The color clashes with your hair," he told her.

She made a face at him and began to scramble through her closet for her shoes. He tapped her on the shoulder and, when she turned, patiently presented her shoes to her. She sat down to pull them on, inquiring, "Do you have your own boat?"

"Umm-hmm. I took her out for the first time this season last weekend. Are you a good sailor?"

She tied her laces and looked up at him, thinking about that. "Well," she decided, "I won't get seasick, if that's what you mean. Actually, I've never been, but it shouldn't be too hard to learn."

His eyes crinkled with silent laughter and he bent to help her to her feet. "My dear," he said, "it looks as though we are both in for an adventure."

AND IT WAS AN ADVENTURE. The drive to the lake took just over an hour, but they stopped for breakfast, and by the time Trey's sleek white sailboat was launched the sun was high in the sky—which was just as well, for Lindsey was just hot enough to appreciate the drenching she got when, trying to follow Trey's complicated directions about the rigging, she caused the boat to careen sharply to the right and almost capsize. That was only the first of a series of near-disastrous mishaps which Trey accepted with patient good humor: She was almost swept overboard by the boom; she missed a collision with another boat by mere inches when she begged Trey to allow her to steer; she became hopelessly entangled in a coil of rope. At last Trey took her shoulders and guided her firmly to sit at the stern, warning her not to move an inch until they were safely in the middle of the lake and away from possible contact with other boats. She meekly accepted the stern tone of his voice and the dancing laughter in his eyes, and the remainder of the journey transpired uneventfully.

The day was tailor-made for sailing. The sky was a clear and endless blue, the wind gentle and consistent, the water a smooth canvas dotted with white sails. There was no sound at all but the faraway drone of speedboats and the gentle lap of water against the hull as, late in the afternoon, Trey lowered the sails and allowed the boat to drift. He removed his jacket and shirt and stretched out on the deck, folding his hands behind his head and advising her that it was her responsibility, as crew, to stand watch while the captain napped. She took her position on the deck chair, but she watched very little other than him. She was already beginning to feel the effects of sunburn on the fair skin of her arms and her nose, and at Trey's command, she wore her jacket and a visored cap he had found for her. The wind ruffled her hair and the sun-reflecting water narrowed her eyes as she gazed at her sleeping captain, an introspective smile on her face. In repose the hard lines of his face smoothed out, his lean bare chest, gleaming with a light film of perspiration, rose and fell peacefully. A day in the sun had turned the hair on his arms to golden against the tawny tan, and she wanted to get up and sit beside him, to run her hands over the taut muscles of those arms and across the strong breadth of his chest. But she didn't. She sat there in the warm glow of the sun and the gentle breeze, and let the undulant motions of the boat rock her into dreamy contentment. Time stretched before her endlessly, and the future was as bright and glistening as the sparkling drops of sunlight on the still lake.

They docked at sundown and had dinner in one of the restaurants on the shore. Several people spoke to Trey when they came in, and Lindsey thought he must come here often. But she noticed he made a point of choosing a darkened table in the corner of the room, and after that they were interrupted by no one except the waiter, who discreetly served and disappeared again.

Trey smiled lazily across the table at her. "You have the cutest little sunburn across your nose, and your eyes are like Caribbean waters. As bright as emeralds and so clear you could see forever."

Her face softened with the unexpected compliment; she told him, "See? You are a poet at heart."

"You bring out the best in me." There was contentment and affection in his eyes as he leaned back and inquired, "Are you tired?"

"Umm-hmm." But it was a good feeling. She glowed all over from the sun and from a quiet happiness, and her body still felt as though it were rocking lazily, creating within her a sense of subtle euphoria. "Oh, Trey," she sighed, "today was marvelous. Thank you."

"Thank you," he corrected, lifting his glass to her,

"for three days of much-needed rest and relaxation. I had forgotten what it was like to have so much fun," he added seriously, looking at her. "I had forgotten how much I needed it. You may," he added on a slightly lighter note, "have just saved my career."

Her eyes widened at this apparent non sequitur. "Oh?"

He nodded, toying with his glass. "Stress. An occupational hazard. I spend all day every day being nice to people, half of whom I don't know and the other half I don't like. It was a relief to relax and be myself for a while. I guess I had forgotten there were still people in the world I could do that with, and I needed the chance to get a few things in perspective. So" — he lifted his glass to her, his eyebrow cocked slightly, a strange little smile on his lips — "to the fate that brought us together."

She touched her glass to his, returning his smile, but then had to point out, "I think it's bad luck to toast with beer. And anyway, you don't believe in fate."

He settled back, still watching her steadily with an amused yet tender look in his eye. "It seems you're always reminding me of things I used to believe in."

"Oh, yes," she quoted him airily, "truth, justice, the tooth fairy—"

"The magic of a spring evening in the country," he continued softly, "dreams that come true and other silly notions...like wishing-stars and leprechauns and that one day a girl would walk into my life and it would never be the same again."

Anticipation clenched suddenly in her throat, she dropped her eyes in confusion. She waited for him to say more, but there was silence. She ventured a glance at him, half-expecting to see teasing in his eyes, but in the flickering candlelight it was impossible to tell what emotion reigned there.

Before anxiety could overtake her, she tried to move the conversation onto more certain ground, and she inquired, "And so what happened?"

He took another sip of his beer, shrugging lightly. "I told you, I grew up. And I got into politics."

She drew in her breath in delighted surprise and started to comment on the coincidence, but something in his face stopped her. His lips tightened slightly as though in self-deprecation, and bitterness crept into his eyes even as he made a light dismissing gesture with his hand.

"It was years ago. My first experience with dirty tricks. I was running for county commissioner, and it was a hot election: organized crime on one hand and crooked politicians on the other. One night I was blissfully dreaming of saving the world and the next morning one woman was threatening me with a paternity suit and another was crying rape—neither of which charges was even remotely accurate, by the way. I discovered my accountant was keeping a double ledger and my campaign manager was robbing me blind. I was offered bribes and threatened with everything from bodily harm to financial ruin. It was my first lesson in the survival of the fittest."

He related the story in such a lighthearted tone that Lindsey knew he meant it to amuse her. She knew only too well of the political corruption which could occur on the local level, although she had never had firsthand experience with it, and she was too aware of the pain such an experience must have caused him to do more than manage a tight smile.

"What did you do?" she prompted.

His lips twisted wryly. "Crushed and disillusioned, I crept off to lick my wounds. I was, you see, to that point a perfect innocent. I took a year to do some hard growing up, and then another position came up on the commission. I gave it another try, older, I thought, and infinitely wiser, ready for anything."

"And?"

He laughed shortly. "I won. Thus began my not-so-illustrious career as a public servant, and that's where it *really* got interesting. Four years later I was never so glad to see anything in my life as my own little full-time private practice."

She said softly, "You shouldn't have let one bad experience make you bitter."

He looked surprised. "I didn't. I'm glad for the experience. I learned a lot—mostly about what I couldn't do, which is just as important to know about yourself as what you can do. It's just that sometimes I look back on myself as I was then and I can't believe I was so naive."

She dropped her eyes sadly, heavy with his pain and disillusionment. "It must be an empty feeling, though," she said, "not to believe in anything."

There was silence. Then his hand moved across the table to take hers. "I'll tell you a secret, Lindsey," he said softly. She looked up at him. There was a deep light in his eyes, and his smile was warm. "I'm starting to believe in you."

Her fingers tightened on his and a warm burst of happiness flooded her like none she had ever known. For the remainder of the meal very little was said, as though each of them knew conversation would be superfluous. For Lindsey, no words could have surpassed that moment of silent discovery when she had looked into his eyes and found trust there.

The warm afterglow of a day perfect in every way stayed with her on the long drive home, during which he held her hand and talked of inconsequential things. It was late, and once again he did not come in.

"It's back to the working world tomorrow, for both of us," he told her, unlocking her door and returning the keys to her. He took her shoulders and kissed her lightly on the forehead. "You get a good night's sleep and impress the hell out of your boss."

She laughed. "That won't be hard to do; he's my uncle."

His eyes crinkled. "That's a smart girl. The quickest way to make it to the top is through friends and relatives." Then he inquired, "Do you like baseball?"

"Love it," she said enthusiastically. At that moment she would have loved anything he suggested.

"I can get tickets to the Houston game Tuesday night, if you'd like."

"Is it being played here?"

His eyes twinkled. "That depends. Say the word and I'll fly the whole lot to Houston for the game. Otherwise, I promise you the best seats in Atlanta Stadium Tuesday night. Your choice."

She tilted her head toward him, her eyes dancing. "I think you're power-crazy."

"And I think you're just plain crazy. Sounds like we have a team." His smile softened as he lifted her chin with his finger, but his kiss was very brief, very gentle. "I'll call you," he promised.

"Do you have my number?" she called after him as he turned to go.

He patted his pocket confidently. "I did a little spying of my own this morning." Once again, his smile filtered tenderly through the darkness toward her. There was reluctance in his voice. "Good night, Lindsey. Sleep well."

She responded softly, "Good night." And she stood at the door and watched until he drove out of sight.

LINDSEY WAS LATE the next morning.

"Traffic," she explained to her brother, "and I had to stop at the bank." She shrugged out of her linen jacket and looked around the busy room for a place to hang it.

Art took the jacket from her, peering at her strangely. "I tried to call you all weekend," he said. "We were supposed to have dinner, remember?"

She had completely forgotten. "I wasn't home," she replied brightly. "I'm sorry. Could we do it tonight instead?"

"Yeah, sure." He turned to hang her jacket and then looked back at her. "So where were you? That's a pretty healthy-looking sunburn."

"I went sailing. Can we clear off a corner of a desk somewhere for me to work? All I need is a typewriter and a telephone."

"Here." He showed her to a desk near the private office. "Put your things here, but I want you to work with Louise for a little while this morning." He looked at her again, trying to keep the brotherly disapproval out of his face. "Who did you go with?" She looked blank, and he specified impatiently, "Sailing."

"Oh." She shrugged lightly. "No one you know."

"Well, I gathered that," he burst out shortly. "I don't like the idea of your going out with strange men, Lindsey."

She smiled secretly, tucking her purse into an empty drawer of the desk. "He wasn't all that strange."

"You know what I mean," he returned curtly, his brows lowering. "You don't know anyone in town but me, and if I didn't introduce you, who did?"

"It's a long story, Art."

"All your stories are." He glanced at his watch impatiently. "And I don't have time for it now. Addison is speaking to a group of police officers tomorrow at breakfast; we need something good on crime by three o'clock. I'm out for the rest of the day. I'll stop by for you here about six; you can tell me your long story over dinner."

"Oh, Miss Madison," Louise called as he left.

"Please, it's Lindsey." With a bright smile Lindsey turned to the older woman. "How are you this morning?"

Louise returned her smile with a small grimace and a shrug. "It's Monday, what can I tell you? You look ready to tackle the world, though."

Lindsey laughed. "I had a marvelous weekend." She felt beautiful. She was wearing her favorite blue pantsuit and she had not used any makeup to cover the glow of sunburn on her face. She had awakened to find that the sun had brought out highlights of gold in her hair and turned her eyes to crystal, and Trey was on her mind. She felt healthy and alert and full of energy, and she knew that before the day was over she would be talking to Trey. Life had never looked so bright to her, and she knew that everything she did today would be magic. She had the Midas touch.

Louise came over to her. "I have that file on Sinclair if you want to go over it now."

Lindsey hesitated. She had just had a brilliant inspiration for the opening of Uncle Addison's speech and she did not want to lose it. "I'll tell you what," she said, touching the other woman's arm lightly. "Give me an hour to draft this speech and we'll go over it together. Get me some information on the other candidates, too, if you can," she added, sliding into her chair and rolling a sheet of paper into the typewriter, "and we'll try to put the whole picture together."

There followed a morning filled with the type of frenetic activity upon which Lindsey thrived. New faces, new names, constant demands, and frequent requests for decisions interrupted the creative process. Lindsey dispatched orders, delegated work, rendered quick, intelligent decisions with automatic ease, answered dozens of questions, and by noon had the respect and friendship of everyone in the office. She finished the draft of the speech while having a sandwich at her desk, and reading over it, she was pleased. She smiled as she thought what a peculiar coincidence it was that her first assignment should be to write a speech on crime after she had just spent the weekend listening to repeated lectures on the subject... and her smile deepened as she thought of Trey.

In the afternoon she and Louise took the folder on Sinclair, along with the condensed biographies on the other candidates, into the private office and closed the door. "Okay," said Lindsey, settling into Addison's large, comfortable chair and opening the folder. "Let's see what kind of dragon this fellow really turns out to be."

Louise drew a chair up near the desk as Lindsey read out loud the top sheet, "John Winston Sinclair III." She lifted an eyebrow. "The third? I didn't know anyone used that anymore." She went on, mostly to herself, "Age thirty-six, single.... That could be a handicap, if he's not careful."

"I think he has his eye on being Washington's most eligible bachelor," put in Louise dryly. "And if he makes it there, he will be, believe me."

Lindsey skimmed the rest of the page. "Only child, Harvard Law School—not bad—two years congressional aide, private law practice—"

"It's not a particularly large firm," put in Louise.

"Mostly they handle corporate business—from his family's corporation, of course. They do have some private cases, not many. You can still see him in the courtroom every once in a while, mostly, I think, to keep in good with the judges."

Lindsey smiled absently and turned the page. "Four years in county government... Do we have a breakdown on his behavior during those four years?"

Louise produced it for her, and Lindsey skimmed it. She did not really expect to find anything, and the report was unremarkable. As Art had warned her, the man's record was impeccable. She skimmed through tax records and financial statements, licenses, permits, and other miscellaneous public documents, which were all in perfect order.

"He's never even gotten a traffic ticket," Lindsey complained. "Doesn't he ever make a mistake?" One of the most important efforts of any campaign was to know the opponent's strengths and weaknesses, his friends and enemies. Only then could they discover for themselves exactly where they stood. Lindsey had never before run across a candidate with so many strengths and so few weaknesses; it was frustrating.

"A man like that is every party's dream," agreed Louise. "They can take him and put him anywhere they want."

"Okay," sighed Lindsey, discarding the material she had already read for a new stack of papers. "Let's see what kind of stand he's taking." Among the copies of his speeches and press releases were the usual fliers and campaign paraphernalia; she started to automatically push those aside. And as she did a campaign poster fell out.

She stared at it. The high forehead, the wave of hair, the sharp nose, the sensitive lips...

Louise, noticing her expression, commented, "Not bad looking, is he? Those eyes are gorgeous. And you wouldn't believe the charisma he has in a crowd—"

Lindsey said shakily, "Oh, God."

Louise's expression sharpened. "Miss Madison?"

Lindsey took a quick breath. She brought her hand somewhat unsteadily to her face, as though to brush away a lock of hair. In a moment she managed, in almost a normal tone, "Do you think there's any coffee left?"

Louise gave her only one more questioning, hesitant look, and she offered, "I'll get it."

When she was gone Lindsey let her shoulders sag; she brought both hands to her face and breathed deeply through her fingers, staring at the innocently accusing photograph on the desk before her. Confusion and shock whirled within her; her mind was going in a hundred frantic directions at once. She knew she had to take hold of herself; she had to sort this out, but she was helpless against the onslaught of emotions which were rushing through her too quickly for her to analyze. How could she have been so stupid? How could she not have known...? But how could she have guessed that the notorious John Winston Sinclair III and a dark-eyed stranger named Trey were one and the same? How *could* she?

She thought back rapidly over the past few days. Surely something he had said, something he had done, should have given her a hint.... Surely, if he had known she was working for the Cantrell campaign, he would have said... But he hadn't known, she realized dully. They had never gotten around to discussing minor details such as that. Up until Friday night he had not even known her last name. And she had thought she knew everything about him....

And then there was anger. Why hadn't he told her? That did seem like the kind of thing he might have at least mentioned. And his name. She was certain he had not told her his last name was Sinclair. She realized slowly he had never told her *what* his last name was. He had introduced his mother and she had just assumed... But his mother had been married three times, and Lindsey should have realized that her name would not necessarily be the same as her son's. She felt like an idiot; she felt like kicking herself, and that only made her angrier. Why hadn't he told her? Why had he kept it such a secret?

But he hadn't kept it a secret, it occurred to her after a moment. He had told her he was in politics, hadn't he? And she had been too careless to question further, she had just assumed that his political career had ended after his four-year term as county commissioner.

"Assumed," she muttered out loud into her clenched hands. "It looks as though you assumed too damn much this time." And then, furious with herself and with him for some unknown reason, she brought her fists down and struck the desk hard. It was a singularly unsatisfying experience, and she hurt her hands.

Louise came in just then with the coffee. "Louise," Lindsey blurted, "I know this man." It was all too much for her to sort out by herself; she had to put it into words. She gestured vaguely toward the picture. "That is, I know him, but not as Sinclair. He told me his name was Trey."

Louise set Lindsey's coffee on the desk, she took her own cup to her chair.

"That's what they call him," she agreed easily, sitting. "Apparently his committee decided the nickname sounded too immature to promote...." And then her gaze sharpened. "You mean," she ventured hesitantly, "you didn't know he was the same...?"

She shook her head bleakly. "We— I was with him this weekend. I—well, we're dating, sort of, and I..." She trailed off miserably. She knew she sounded like just as much of a fool as she felt.

"My goodness." Louise sank back in her chair, looking at Lindsey in amazement. "I've been in politics thirty years and I don't believe anything like this has *ever* happened."

Lindsey managed a small, weak smile. "It could only happen to me."

Louise said suddenly, "Does he know you're working for Cantrell?"

Lindsey shook her head impatiently. "How could he? *My* picture isn't exactly posted in every window in town, and it never occurred to me to mention..." She bit her lip, angry and confused. "Well, anyway, how could I have known? I've only been in town a week, and Uncle Addison never sent me any pictures of the opposition. How was I to know his mother had a different last name?" And, far away in the back of her mind a small, secret voice taunted her, *That's what you get for picking up strangers....* She didn't know whether she wanted to burst into tears or throw something.

Louise's eyes twinkled; she was having difficulty restraining laughter. "I'm sorry dear," she said, "but it *is* an incredible story, and it doesn't sound as though any harm was done. It's a shame, though." She glanced again at the campaign poster with a sigh. "I don't suppose there's a woman in this state who wouldn't have liked to be in your shoes this weekend, and now you have to give it all up. It will be like Cinderella returning from the ball."

Lindsey looked at her, a new confusion cutting through the old one. "What do you mean?"

"Well, naturally, when he finds out..." She shrugged, letting the sentence finish itself.

Lindsey sank back. She had been so wrapped up in her own indignation and confusion she had never given a thought to the future. "I—I guess I have to tell him," she managed, somewhat dazedly.

Louise gave a short laugh. "I should think so! How else is he going to find out?" And then she hesitated, her expression growing thoughtful. "Then again... for all his mild-mannered appearance, I don't believe our Mr. Sinclair is the type of person who takes too well to being made a fool of—and that's how it's going to appear, you know, no matter how innocent your part in it has been. It might be better not to give him any reason at all, if he wants to see you again."

Lindsey felt as though her entire world were spinning out of control. She anchored her eyes on Louise's competent face. "You mean—not see him again?"

Louise seemed surprised. "Well, I don't see that you have any choice. Anything else would be unethical—for you and him."

"I—I guess so."

Louise fastened her eyes on Lindsey's stricken, slightly distracted features, and a puzzled frown touched her own face. "Miss Madison... Lindsey," she corrected, her tone softening. "I know this is none of my business, but... how seriously are you involved with him?"

Lindsey sat back, swallowing hard, and a slight shake of her head was only a surface indication of the bewilderment which was rampaging through her. How seriously? Yesterday... yesterday she could have answered that question. Yesterday she would have given the world for his smile. Yesterday had been the happiest, the most contented, the most secure of her life. And now...

"I don't know," she answered softly.

"It really is an incredible situation," Louise reminded her.

Lindsey tried to smile. "I know." Then she looked up at her. "Louise, would you...not mention this to my brother or to Uncle Addison?" When all else was utter uncertainty, this one thing was clear. "I feel kind of silly."

Louise smiled at her reassuringly. "Of course not." And she added, her eyes softening with sympathy, "You look kind of sad."

Lindsey whispered, "I guess I am."

She went to the restroom and splashed cold water on her cheeks; the sunburn was suddenly painful. She patted her face dry with a paper towel, and then forced herself to take a stern look in the mirror, determined to seize some measure of control over the situation. Finally, she even managed a dry smile at the stark-eyed, red-cheeked girl who stared back at her. Louise thought it was funny. Well, maybe it was. Trey might even laugh when she told him. Trey might laugh...but she did not know what John Winston Sinclair would do.

It didn't seem fair. Just as she was getting to know him, just as she was making discovery after wonderful discovery about him, that their relationship should arbitrarily be cut short. It wasn't her fault that this had happened; it simply wasn't fair.

Two things haunted her throughout that busy afternoon: the fact that she desperately wanted to see him again, and Louise's innocent comment, "If you don't tell him, how else is he going to find out?" She did not know what to do.

She plunged into her work, reading everything she could about him and sending researchers out for more information. Whatever else had happened, one thing had not changed. She was still working for Addison Cantrell, and she still had an election to win. She summed up her findings for Art over dinner. "He takes a very hard stand on crime," she said. "I'm thinking we'd better strengthen our position on that. He has come out strongly for budget cuts, especially in social programs."

"Political suicide," interjected Art, attacking his steak with enthusiasm.

"Well, you've got to admit, he's not afraid to take a stand." Lindsey tried to keep the admiration out of her tone. All day long she had been trying to resolve her personal impression of Trey with her professional one. As was to be expected, there were many issues upon which they hotly disagreed and some, surprisingly, upon which they agreed. All in all, she had found nothing to diminish her opinion of him and a great deal to improve it. "Did you know," she commented innocently, "that he was working for the Equal Rights Ammendment before he was publicly political?"

"That won't help him a bit," replied Art confidently. "The voters of this state already have shown they don't want ERA."

"The *legislators* of this state have shown it," she corrected.

"Same thing," he returned. "Did *you* know that he made a rather rash statement some years back in support of the legalization of marijuana?"

She took a quick sip of her wine, swallowing her surprise. "No, I didn't," she said. That was one controversial issue no politician wanted to tackle, not unless he were very sure of his position. "I can't believe he would be so foolish."

"Well," admitted Art, "perhaps the original statement wasn't exactly a call to arms, but with a little rewording here and there..."

Lindsey set her glass carefully on the white tablecloth. "What," she inquired distinctly, "exactly are you saying?"

Art caught the flash in his sister's eyes, the tautening of her face. He lowered his fork and touched his napkin to his lips. His expression was very serious.

"Look," he said quietly, "it's time we started looking at this thing for what it is. Sinclair is a strong candidate. He's young, he's energetic, he's got personality to spare. He's an expert on foreign affairs and a financial genius, he's strong on domestic policy and the courts. It doesn't hurt that his family is one of the most well-known names in this state and that his father spent most of his life in state government. He can make all sorts of wild promises and support them from his own background and make the people think, 'Yes, by God, this is the man we want in Washington; he'll have the country turned around inside a month.' He can make people *believe* in him, Lindsey, don't you see? And if that's his strongest point, then that's where we're going to hit."

"Make the voters question his credibility," elucidated Lindsey flatly.

"Yes," responded Art, unflinching.

She took a breath. She drew her eyes away from Art's and tried to remain calm. "I think you're making much ado about nothing. This is his first time for national office, and he's running against an incumbent. He doesn't have the experience...."

Art gave her a peculiar look. "You know this game well enough to know you have to stay at least three steps ahead of the play at all times. We're preparing for the worst. I don't like to run a smear campaign any more than you do—it has a way of backfiring—but if things get desperate enough, I'm not going to be afraid to do it."

"You try it," Lindsey said lowly, her eyes very steady, "and you'll do it without me. This is going to be a clean race, Arthur."

He sat back, watching her cautiously. "What are you going to do, wait for him to pull the first punch?"

"He won't," she answered shortly.

"How can you be so sure?"

Because he's too honest, Lindsey thought with quiet assurance, but she said nothing. A small, cold feeling started in the pit of her stomach as she began to realize for the first time what she had gotten herself into. Trey trusted her, but she was the opposition. What would he think if he found out? More political games? Would he relegate her to the same category in which he had placed those unscrupulous characters who had ruined his first campaign? She did not think she could bear that.

Art apparently sensed the need for a tactical retreat. He took up his knife and fork again. "So. Have you heard anything from Dad lately?"

"No." She had, as a matter of fact, received a letter just before she left, filled with enthusiasm about a new project he had begun and best wishes for her new venture; it was rather disjointed in the delightful way which was so typical of her father when he took pen in hand, but it was nothing which would interest Art.

"Well," he said pleasantly, "tell me about this new man in your life. You certainly don't waste any time, do you?"

That was more than she could take just then. She inwardly recoiled at what Art's reaction would be if he really knew about the new man in her life, and she knew right then more clearly than she had ever known anything in her life that she would never be able to discuss Trey with Art. It was an instinct which was protective in nature and darkly intuitive, and somehow it made her angry. She had never kept secrets from her brother before. "I've managed my life quite well without you for twenty-nine years, Arthur," she said coolly. "Please don't start interfering now."

Arthur looked surprised, but said nothing. The remainder of the meal was finished in stiff silence, and Lindsey was miserable.

As they prepared to go, Art caught her hand, a look of apology on his face. "I didn't mean to make you angry," he said. "Addison has been the people's choice for twelve years and his record speaks for itself; I just don't want anything to blow it now. We've never had to use underhanded tactics, and I don't want to start now. Believe me, Lindsey, I don't. We'll fight fair as long as Sinclair does. But I just want you to know we've got to be open to all possibilities. This is not going to be like any other campaign you've ever run, and we are *not* going to lose."

Lindsey agreed with him silently and rather bleakly on two points: This was not like any other campaign, and she was not going to lose.

AT NINE THIRTY Trey called. "Hi," he said. "I'm between two meetings and I can't talk long—I just wanted you to know I keep my promises."

Lindsey's breath had caught in her throat at the first sound of his voice; all of a sudden a thousand unexpected emotions were pelleting her and she had difficulty speaking; she could not even think. "P-promises?"

"Sure," he responded easily. "I promised I would call you, remember?"

She sank weakly into a chair, holding the phone with both hands, closing her eyes against a softening smile. His voice, so familiar, yet different because it belonged to another man—John Winston Sinclair, her sworn enemy. But the words were still Trey's, the thoughtfulness, the sentiment—all of it belonged to the man she thought she knew; her two images of him became all mixed up inside her, and she did not know whether the small pain she felt far away in the pit of her stomach was from happiness or despair. "I remember," she said softly.

There was a brief pause. "You sound tired. Rough day at the office?"

She gave a choked-off laugh. "Like you wouldn't believe."

"Same here. As a matter of fact, I'm keeping a committee waiting now. I'd better go."

She managed brightly, "Committee? At this time of night?" But she knew only too well what the schedule of a politician was. She imagined Addison Cantrell would not see his bed before midnight either.

"Such is life. Shall I pick you up about seven tomorrow night?"

Her stunned silence gave her away, and he gave an exasperated laugh. "You didn't forget our date, did you?"

"No," she said quickly. "Of course not." She had forgotten. "Seven is fine. I'll be ready."

"I'll see you then." But he seemed reluctant to say good-bye. The seconds ticked off while she clutched the receiver and prayed he wouldn't hang up. The contact with him, even through the miles of telephone wire, seemed to her at that moment a lifeline. Then he said softly, "Lindsey...I thought about you all day today. That's a first for me."

Her breath was tight and rapid, her voice a little high. Her fingers dug into the hard plastic of the telephone "Oh?"

"To let a woman take my mind off my work. I don't know whether that's good or bad."

She whispered, "Good, I hope."

She heard his long, soft breath. Then he said, "I really have to go. I'll see you tomorrow."

She said, very softly, "Good night."

She replaced the receiver slowly, staring at it, and the expression on her face was pained and introspective. She really couldn't have told him over the phone. She would have to tell him eventually, but so soon... They had only just begun, how could she let something which felt so special to her be snatched away without ever giving it a chance? It just wasn't fair.

Everything had happened between them so quickly, how could she be sure what was real and what wasn't? They needed more time, time together to know each other and discover one another...and what would happen if she told him the truth? She really didn't know. He might understand. He might feel compelled to break off the relationship for ethical reasons. He might not even believe that it had all been a mistake....

She tossed and turned fretfully in her half-sleep, and in the morning nothing was clearer. She only knew that she wanted to see him again, and that, above all, she could not bear it if Trey ever thought she had betrayed him.

SHE SAW HIM on television the next evening. It was a paid political announcement following the six o'clock news, and Lindsey's first reaction, after the instinctual shock at seeing the man she had thought to have known so intimately on television, was the bitter reflection that if she had just once bothered to turn on her television during the past week she wouldn't be in the mess she was in now. Her second reaction was a cautious admiration for the talent which had put together the spot, for it was perfectly beautiful. No wonder Art was so worried, if Trey had resources like that backing him.

The sixty-second spot included no less than a dozen widely varied scenes, during which Trey, in a denim workshirt and hard hat, mingled with a group of construction workers, discussing their problems seriously; then in jeans and a checked shirt he examined soil with a farmer; again he made a few pertinent and down-to-earth comments on the economy at a union meeting. There was one scene showing his enthusiastic reception on the campaign trail, shaking hands with a wildly responsive crowd, laughing and joking and capturing every heart there with an easy smile and sure eye contact. Lindsey realized in amazement that she had never known that side of him; she was reminded poignantly of his words, "I'm a professional charmer," and she was both awed and disheartened. How could he make it look so *genuine*? It ended with another outdoor scene, Trey sitting casually on the steps of the Federal Building—perfect symbolism—and addressing his audience one-to-one in capable, confident terms. How could anyone resist the sincerity in those mesmerizing dark eyes, the subtle aura of strength and control as he sat there assuring you that he understood your problems, cared about them, and was going to do something about them?

"Lord," Lindsey murmured to herself as it ended, "he's almost got *me* convinced to vote for him." And the professional side of her mind was thinking efficiently, *He's got flair. Panache. Colorful backgrounds and active scenes. We'll counter with sobriety. Dark suits and straight talk. The flag and eagle. Solidity and permanence, as steady as a rock all the way*.... And she absently made her way across the room to answer the persistent ringing of the doorbell.

Trey stood there, casually dressed, smiling easily. In a moment of disorientation, she tried to resolve the confused images of the television politician with the flesh-and-blood incarnation who stood before her now, and she simply gaped at him.

At his questioning glance, she burst out without thinking, "I just saw you on television!"

He lifted an eyebrow and stepped inside. "Is that right? How did I look?"

She thought of him shaking hands and flinging out promises and she could only stammer, "D-different."

He answered offhandedly, "I understand the camera puts on ten pounds," and she simply stared at him.

Something in her confused stance must have communicated itself to him, for he turned to her with a peculiar look just as she exclaimed, again without thinking, "But—you never told me you were running for office."

The brows lifted sharply in surprise, the look in his eyes was at first denial, then confusion, then, finally, amused introspection. "You know, I guess I didn't. I just assumed you knew."

"You just assumed!" Automatic indignation, completely unjustified, snapped within her. Whatever reaction she had expected from him, this was not it. She had spent too much agony over the discovery to have him take it so lightly. She demanded, "How could you just assume? Why didn't you tell me?"

"Well..." Amusement still sparkled in his eyes. "I

suppose it didn't occur to me. But I'll remedy that right now." He stepped forward and extended his hand, "Hello, I'm John Sinclair, running for U.S. Senate. Appreciate your vote."

She was not amused. She said sharply, "It does seem as though I'm the only person in the state you haven't gotten around to hitting on for a vote. What's the matter, didn't you think I was old enough?"

The laughter faded from his eyes. A momentary disturbance crossed his face which was too complicated for Lindsey, in her high emotional state, to read. And then he simply dropped his hand onto her shoulder and suggested, "Come on. We'll miss the first ball."

Lindsey tried to improve her mood during the game, but she was not very successful. She found herself suspiciously watching Trey for some signs of the instant charm she had witnessed on television, but he did not attempt to do any campaigning that night. His smile, she noticed, was friendly and general, and his manner to the strangers who recognized him was receptive but not pushy. His entire attitude was that of a man who is accustomed to being aware of his public image without actively calling attention to it, and Lindsey was not certain whether this was a new role he assumed for only large gatherings, or whether it had been there all along and she had simply never noticed it before. She tried not to let it irritate her. He was certainly very careful not to do anything which might irritate her. If he noticed her moodiness, he did not draw attention to it, and his attitude toward her was light and natural, as though he were nothing more than a man out to enjoy himself at a ball game. Just as she was beginning to relax and enjoy his company, telling herself she was really being silly about the whole thing, two of his aides came over. Trey did not introduce them as aides, but

Lindsey knew that was what they were. They did not stay long and did not talk about business at all, but nonetheless, Lindsey found it harder to pretend to enjoy herself after that.

This thing is going to tear me apart, she thought bleakly on the drive home. *I've got to tell him, to get it out in the open, otherwise it's only going to get worse, for both of us.* But at the door she hesitated, uncertain whether to invite him in or not.

He solved that problem for her by ushering her inside ahead of him and closing the door behind them. "Thank you, I'd love some coffee," he responded to a question she had no intention of asking. "Mind if I sit down?"

"Trey," she began hesitantly, "I really have a hard day tomorrow...." *Not tonight,* she thought. *I really don't want to go into it with him tonight. Later, after the shock has worn off and I can really look at this thing clearly...*

He arranged himself in the green chair with a negligent ease, and his eyes held a subtle challenge. She went to put on the coffee.

"So," he inquired when she returned, "have I suddenly grown horns and a tail, or are you just so impressed you don't know how to behave around me anymore?" The question was casual, but the arrangement of his body was tense, and in his eyes, far from their customary frankness, was an uneasiness she had never glimpsed there before.

She sat stiffly on the edge of the sofa across from him, smoothing her hands on her knees. She tried to look pleasant. "I don't know what you mean."

He made an abrupt gesture of impatience with his wrist. "Yes, you do. It's because you've found out I'm in politics, which to you, I imagine, is the epitome of corruption and self-degradation." His tone became bitter, defensive. "I only hope I haven't soiled you with my presence."

She gaped at him. "No! It's not that at all! I—as a matter of fact, I'm interested in politics...." She should have told him. Right then and there, he had given her the opening, and she should have told him. The words would not come out.

His face relaxed into a tentative relief, though it was mixed with regret. "Then it's because you think I deliberately deceived you. Believe me, Lindsey, I didn't. I honestly didn't think...I'm so used to people knowing who I am, and you never questioned me on anything, you just seemed to know. The subject never really came up, I suppose and it didn't occur to me that you might be hurt by not knowing."

Such sincerity in his tone, such apology in his eyes... He was afraid *she* was accusing *him* of deception. What whould he say if he knew that even now she was plotting to deceive him? The thought clenched at her stomach, and she had to get up quickly and go to the kitchen. "No," she reassured him quickly. "It's not that. I'm not...hurt, or angry or anything, it's just... that it was such a shock...."

He followed her, standing close behind her as she poured the coffee. "I really hope you mean that, Lindsey," he said soberly. "Because I'm committed to this campaign." And then he smiled. "I told you I was a professional charmer, didn't I? You can't really say I didn't warn you."

No, she couldn't say that.... Her hand shook and coffee sloshed onto the counter. She reached for a sponge and began to busily mop it up.

"It all looks very impressive," she said brightly, trying not to chatter. "I mean, your speeches, your television commercial...very nice. I heard"—she cleared her throat a little—"some of your stands, but you're not really tackling all the issues publicly, are you? And how much of it is just hype, and how much do you really mean?"

A small frown touched his brow as he accepted his cup of coffee from her. "I mean everything I say, Lindsey."

"I heard..." She stirred her coffee busily, although she had never added cream or sugar. "I heard that you were just a tool of the party, a figurehead, just a clotheshorse they could use to get what they wanted."

Now his brows lifted in surprise. "Where did you hear *that*?"

Yes, where would she have heard it, if she had only this evening learned about his campaign? She was floundering over her head. She changed tactics.

"So," she demanded with assumed lightness, "how do you really feel about women's rights?"

"I'm all for them." He was watching her strangely. She blundered on.

"Of course, what politician wouldn't be? And what about all this stuff about reforming government programs to reduce government spending? How do you feel about all the cuts to the arts and humanities? What's going to happen to Social Security? What about—"

He laughed helplessly, dropping his arm about her shoulders. "Whoa, there. I think you'd better stop before I'm forced to say something very chauvinistic."

Something about his touch was like a tranquilizer. The tension and the animosity drained out of her. She looked up at him as he led the way to the living area and even found herself smiling naturally. "Like what?"

"Like"—he dropped a light kiss on her hair—"don't bother your pretty little head about politics, miss. Leave the thinking to the men."

She stiffened, even though she knew he was teasing, and moved away from him to sit on the sofa. "Well?" she demanded somewhat coolly, looking him straight in the eye. "Are you a tool of the party?"

He took his coffee to the chair opposite, and he sat there for a time, sipping it thoughtfully, watching her. At last he answered, "I'm allowing myself to be used to achieve mutual goals."

"In words of one syllable, please," she returned shortly. "My pretty little head isn't capable of much deep thinking, you know."

He acknowledged her rejoinder with a brief, vague smile. His expression quickly fell to seriousness again. "The party is using me," he admitted, "but I'm also using it. Because I want this position."

"Why?" she insisted, and her expression was one of genuine bafflement. This, she knew, was the real question which had been bothering her since yesterday. Nothing she had known about Trey in any way qualified him as the type of person who would seek political office. He had no fiery ambitions, no thirst for power, no need of money, and he had seemed generally content with his life. "Why?" she repeated.

He dropped his eyes briefly, and then smiled at her. "At first because it was convenient. When the party approached me, I thought, Why not? I'm a pretty good candidate—I'm honest, I have a certain standard of integrity, and, as far as I can tell, I'm fairly incorruptible, which puts me one up on most of the other men in the running. Washington appealed to me. My father was always active in government, and I suppose I inherited some of his bent toward that tradition. But lately"—he looked at her; his expression was very sober, his voice quiet—"I've come to think there might have been another reason I agreed to run, one I didn't want to admit even to myself. Since meeting you, Lindsey, I've been reminded that I do have a few dreams left. Ideals that I still care about, somewhere deep inside, enough to want to see them made reality. I really believe that I can change things, and I want to try."

A sudden aching began deep within her; she lowered her eyes against the unexpected sting of tears. She wanted to hold him then. She wanted to get up and stumble into his arms and feel, through his embrace, that everything was going to be all right. But instead she sipped her coffee, looking up at him, and smiled, bravely and falsely. *Washington appeals to me, too, Trey,* she thought bleakly. *I have dreams and ideals, and I want a chance to change things, too. The only trouble is, only one of us can go.*

She wanted to cry.

ONE THING BECAME CLEAR in the ensuing days. She could not tell him, not right away. How could she tell him that she, the one person he trusted and had recently come to believe in, could single-handedly undermine his campaign and was fully and unquestionably committed to the opposition? How would he react? How could she take a chance on hurting him? How could she possibly have grown to care about him so much in such a short time, and how could she take a chance on losing him?

She began to rationalize it. It wasn't her fault that this dreadful thing had happened. And really, their seeing one another wasn't such a crime. She was still dedicated to Addison Cantrell for senator and nothing would change that. Trey was still a strong contender, and he would be with or without her. They were just two people who enjoyed being with one another and were beginning to care about one another, and there was no reason their personal lives had to intrude into their professional, or vice versa. After all, she began to realize as her usual confidence and optimism returned, there were hundreds of people working on the Cantrell campaign, and she was only one of them. There were dozens of contenders for this senate seat, and Trey was only one of them. It needn't be such a big problem at all. It didn't really even have to come up between them at all, at least not until after the August primaries, and August was a very long time away. By then, a lot could have changed.

And so she let it slip past, a little at a time, day by day, and soon she forgot all the reasons it had seemed so urgent to tell him in the first place. Just being with him was all she needed.

Bob Cagle came into Trey's office late one afternoon less than a week later. Trey was in a hurry; he was due to speak at a dinner in half an hour and he had a date with Lindsey at eight. He would probably be late for both of them. He was on the phone when Bob came in; one of his aides had just delivered his speech; he had just taken a moment to change his shirt and was trying to tie his tie one-handed while he read the speech and finished his telephone conversation.

He said to Bob as he hung up, "If it's not important, it will have to wait." He jerked off his tie and redid it properly, using the window as a mirror. "I haven't got time to deal with anything right now less important than the imminent collapse of the Free World."

"Well, I'm not sure how important it is," responded Bob carefully. "That's why I wanted to talk to you."

Trey did not glance up as he picked up his speech and began to button his cuffs. "Thirty seconds."

"Do you know that girl you were with at the ball game?"

"Lindsey?" Trey ran his hand over his face and thought he probably needed a shave. He wondered if he had time. "What about her?"

"Didn't I see you with her once before, in the garage?"

Trey glanced up. "Yes. I guess you did." He glanced at his watch and pushed away from his desk. "Bob, is there a point—"

"I thought you might like to know more about her."

Trey hesitated, a frown of irritation creasing his features. "What is this?"

"Look," Bob said with a sigh, "I know you've been seeing a lot of her...."

Trey's eyes sharpened. He sat back cautiously. "I don't remember hiring you to spy—much less on me."

There was no visible change of expression on Bob's face. It was polite, respectful, remote, and just the slightest bit concerned. "It's part of the job." He produced a manila file and presented it to Trey.

Trey did not know whether to be amused or angry. His expression, as he took the folder, was somewhere between the two. "What did you do, run an FBI check?"

"No," answered Bob, perfectly serious. "But I can, if you like."

Trey half-chuckled as he flipped open the folder. He would read it later, just for fun, and Lindsey might get a kick out of it when he showed her. She had such a childlike interest in what went on behind the political scenes, he would enjoy her reaction when she discovered she had been investigated as part of the cam-

paign. He read absently, scanning it, "Madison, Lindsey Eleanor, Ph.D., age twenty-nine..." And then his
eyes flickered back. "Ph.D?" He glanced at Bob, and
got no reaction. He was not even certain what his own
reaction was—something between amusement and astonishment. But then, nothing about Lindsey really
surprised him anymore, she was without a doubt the
most fascinating female he had ever met. And then he
read on. "Doctorate in political science...."

Something cold knotted within him; he did not look
up, but neither did he read on for a moment. He tried
to take a moment to sort it out, to push away the dread
that was forming irrationally on some deep-seated
level. She had told him she taught at a university,
hadn't she? He shouldn't be so surprised. A great
many university professors had doctorates, and he had
never underestimated Lindsey's intelligence. He remembered the tasteless teasing comment he had made
about "not bothering her pretty little head" and he
groaned inwardly. She should have told him what her
specialty was, but then again, he had never asked. He
had been too involved discovering more important
things about her...

"Mr. Sinclair." Bob interrupted his rather distracted
thoughts gently. "I think you should read on."

And then he did. Slowly, his jawline hardened, his
lips compressed. Color drained from his face and the
fingers which clenched the paper tightened until the
knuckles shone white and the paper creased and crumpled. He stared at it for a long time, and he said nothing.

The silence became oppressive, and at last Bob felt
he had to break it. "Apparently Cantrell has promised
her a job as his aide in Washington if he's re-elected.

That's one sharp lady there, Mr. Sinclair, and she has a lot at stake.''

Slowly, and with great deliberation, Trey placed the paper on the desk. He smoothed out the creases in two careful movements, and then he sat back, his eyes dark but his face a perfect blank, and stared at a point just beyond Bob's head. He said simply, "I see."

"Then," ventured Bob, "you didn't have any idea...?"

A small, bitter smile touched Trey's lips. "Arthur Madison," he said softly. "I used to play golf with him. I should have made the connection...." Why *hadn't* he made the connection? He, who was usually so careful, had fallen right into her trap. He hadn't known anything about her because he hadn't asked anything about her; he had broken all of his own rules and he deserved to be played for the fool. Now, of all times, and with her, of all people....

And then he laughed shortly. "Well, she did tell me she was working for her uncle."

Bob looked hesitant. As much as anyone could really know Trey Sinclair, he had thought he knew him. But he had never seen Trey look like this. It made him very uneasy. He cleared his throat, "I think the best way to handle this—"

Trey's eyes flashed on him sharply. "I'll handle it."

"You can't mean you're going to continue to see her," Bob burst out incredulously. "She's a spy, a high-caliber political professional—you can't take chances—"

"Damn it, I said I would handle it!" Trey exploded at him, his face darkening and his eyes snapping fire. Bob literally took a step backward, stunned into silence.

Slowly, the dark flush receded from Trey's face, his hooded eyes grew calmer. But still Bob did not relax. He had never seen Trey like this, and the cold, mirthless smile which spread over his face was almost as frightening as the anger. "I'm not a complete fool," Trey said softly, almost to himself. "I just act like one sometimes."

And then Trey looked at Bob; something of a more customary expression touched his face, the smile became almost human again. He said, "If you're worried I'm going to spill campaign secrets to her in bed, don't. She may be sharp, but I'm sharper. As a matter of fact, I wouldn't worry about Miss Lindsey Madison at all as far as the campaign goes; whatever she's up to, it won't work. It might, however," he added, rising, "be interesting to see just exactly what she did have in mind... and how far she was willing to go to get what she wanted."

Bob said, helping Trey into his jacket, "I'm sorry to have to tell you this. I can see you're upset."

Trey looked at him and managed a reassuring smile. "I'm not upset about the campaign. No harm done, and no danger. As a matter of fact, I really can't believe Cantrell would be stupid enough to think something like this would work. I just," he added—and the smile faded as he reached for the door; his tone grew grim— "don't like to be lied to."

Chapter Seven

Trey was late, but Lindsey was glad. She had only gotten home a half hour earlier herself, and she rushed through her shower and blow-drying her hair. She should have been exhausted and ready for bed after a day such as she had had, but simply knowing she was going to see Trey gave her a new burst of energy. She would have waited for him until midnight if need be and happily danced until dawn without ever feeling any ill effects.

She stepped into a green jump suit and then was not at all certain it was the correct thing to wear. The material was a featherlight, almost netlike metallic knit; it hugged her curves revealingly and the sharp neckline plunged almost to midabdomen. But the rich color *did* make her eyes look like emeralds, and she liked the way it glittered when she walked. She hesitated over the deep cut of the neckline that swept back to reveal more than a little of her breasts and a spattering of freckles on her chest, but then it was too late to change because the doorbell was ringing.

She was trying to fasten an earring as she flung open the door, saying breathlessly, "I'm almost ready. Just another second."

His eyes swept over her once, and if she had not been so busy with the uncooperative earring, she would have been chilled at the look in those eyes. But he simply stepped in and closed the door, saying, "I'm a little late. I couldn't break away."

She missed the curt tone in his voice as she hurried to a mirror, responding cheerfully, "Oh, that's okay, I'm always late. Just give me another minute...." She turned to the mirror and struggled with the stubborn earring which wouldn't clasp.

For a moment he stood in the center of the room, watching her with a dark, contemplative look that would have terrified her had she seen it. Then he said abruptly, "Do you have anything to drink?"

She glanced at him, for the fist time noticing something peculiar in his manner. She answered, "Some wine, I think. And fruit juice."

"I don't want wine." But he went to the kitchen and opened the refrigerator, taking out the remainder of the bottle of wine they had shared the evening before and searching for a glass. "Don't you keep anything stronger?"

She turned back to the mirror. "Why should I? You know I don't drink the stuff."

"What about your brother?" He practically spat the words out as he sloshed some of the wine into a glass. "Don't you keep anything around for him?" When he turned to her, raising his glass, his eyes were very cold.

She abandoned her efforts with the earring. A little chill of confusion went through her as she looked at him. She wasn't certain exactly what she saw in his eyes, but it took her back unpleasantly to their first meeting—remoteness, mistrust, and perhaps, far below the surface, an intense dislike. But she gave a little laugh and said, "My brother is not known for his sociable traits. If he were to ever stop by for a 'friendly drink' the last thing I would be worried about is what to serve him.''

"Oh?" His eyes glittered. "What would you be worried about?"

Her laugh grew nervous. "What he wanted, probably." And then she started toward him, concerned. "Trey..."

He emptied the glass in two gulps, setting the glass on the counter and meeting her in the center of the room.

"Here." He snatched the earring from her. "Let me do that." He pushed back her hair and inserted the wire through her pierced ear swiftly and urgently, pinching her tender skin as he clasped it.

"Ouch," she said, pulling away, startled.

His smile was short and bitter and did not reach his eyes. "Sorry." His grasp on her arm was every bit as rough as his ministrations with the earring had been. "Shall we go?"

THEY WENT to the Limelight Club, famed haunt of such personalities as Kenny Rogers and Burt Reynolds. Neither one of those celebrities showed up that night, however, and though Lindsey did her best to keep the mood festive, she could not remember spending a more uncomfortable evening. Trey did not want to dance; he did not talk much and gave only perfunctory replies to her rather desperate attempts to make conversation. He nursed the same drink all evening without taking more than one or two sips from it, and his eyes kept darting about the room, as though looking for some way to escape. Finally, about ten o'clock, he said abruptly, "Let's go."

"But," she protested, rising, and not knowing what

else to say, "you haven't even finished your drink! You've hardly touched it."

He glanced at the glass with a mirthless smile as he tossed a couple of bills on the table. "That's all I need, isn't it? To be picked up for DUI? The perfect end to a perfect day, as I believe you might have said once."

She followed him, bewildered, across the room. She noticed that he did not touch her once.

In the car he said stonily, "I won't be seeing you"—he had fully intended to say "again"; he was surprised when the words came out—"for a while."

She turned startled eyes on him in the filtering flash of a street light. "Why?"

He shrugged, reaching for a pack of cigarettes he had almost forgotten was on the dashboard. "The campaign trail beckons. Those are the breaks when you're hooked up with a politician."

He struck a match and lit the cigarette, and the yellow glow of the flame showed her a hard profile which she almost did not recognize as the man she had spent every free hour with for the past two weeks. She stared at him.

"I didn't know you smoked," she said in amazement.

The look he gave her was sharp and brief, and he tapped the cigarette on the edge of the ashtray viciously. "There's a lot you don't know about me," he returned shortly, and Lindsey relapsed into silence, hurt and totally confused.

She thought surely he wouldn't come inside with her. Whatever had caused his dark mood, she had gotten the distinct impression that she was only aggravating it, and she thought he would want to be away from her as quickly as possible. She was surprised when, he not only followed her in but took off his jacket and tossed it on a chair. That was a gesture totally unlike

Trey, not so much casual as rude, presumptuous and suggestive. He loosened his tie and lit another cigarette. Again she only stared at him. She felt as though she were with a total stranger.

"I'll put on some coffee," she volunteered, and he neither agreed nor objected as she went into the kitchen.

When she returned, he was sitting on the sofa, smoking moodily. When he saw her, he crushed out the cigarette and patted the place on the sofa beside him. For just that moment he looked almost like himself, as though he were ready to relax and confide in her. She went to him gratefully, but as soon as she sat beside him she felt him retreat from her, the unfathomable expression was back in his eyes again. Trying to find a way to break through his reserve, she inquired, "When are you leaving?"

He draped his arm along the back of the sofa, but it was not a gesture of affection. His posture was tense and alert, he watched her like a cat at a mousehole. It made her very nervous. He answered, "Tomorrow, I suppose."

Such short notice! She knew that these things were planned months in advance, and he could have told her.... She tried to swallow her disappointment with a smile, and she asked, "How long will you be gone?"

"I don't know. Six, eight weeks. Maybe longer. Too long, I know that." The words were reassuring, more like the old Trey, but just as Lindsey was warming to them she saw the coldness in the twist of his lips which was not quite a smile, as though his intention was to push her away, not draw her closer. "You could come with me," he suggested, and the very absence of genuine warmth in the invitation made it sound like an insult.

She replied, managing a smile, "You know I can't."

"Of course." His voice was silky, his lids drooped lazily over his eyes. "It wouldn't do at all, would it? The two of us living in sin on the campaign trail—think of the scandal."

Every word he spoke plunged her deeper into a despair of confusion. She cast desperately about in her mind for some way to draw him out of this ugly mood, to reach again the part of him that she knew. But her only resource was the direct approach, and it was long overdue. "Trey," she demanded gently, "what's the matter with you? Why are you acting like this?"

"Don't you know?" Slowly, his fingers insinuated themselves beneath her hair, along the bare column of her neck, stroking, massaging, exploring with a deft strength which hinted of barely restrained violence. An uncontrollable, hot shiver went down her spine even as her first instinct was self-protective—to move away from him quickly, before whatever was driving him pushed them both into something they would soon regret.

But she sat there as though mesmerized as the pressure upon the back of her neck steadily increased, slowly tilting her head upward toward him, and his face moved closer by inches.

He said huskily, "You know you wore that outfit tonight just to make me crazy...just to let me see what I don't have...and it is driving me crazy, Lindsey...."

The force of his mouth was brutal, punishing, totally unlike Trey. His teeth bruised her lips and her first reaction was a muffled cry of protest that was lost within the hard force of his mouth. There was no tenderness here, no gentleness or caring, but passion perverted into violence, expressing hatred and not love. She struggled against it indignantly, and brought her hand up to push him away, but his fingers closed about her wrist in a viselike grip, crushing her hand between their bodies as his weight forced her down on the sofa.

And then, all at once, it changed. As though triggered in each of them by the full contact of their bodies, passion flamed and exploded, washing over her in a red-hot haze, tensing in each of her muscles building into an aching need which was fast escalating out of control. She felt his startled, unsteady breath, and when his mouth took hers again the demand was no more gentle than it had been before, but violence had changed to urgency, mindless and instinctual, and she responded helplessly. Her free arm crept about his neck while his hand left her neck to slip inside her jump suit and clasp her breast. The pressure of his fingers was hard and his caress was rough; it drew a breathless sound from her of a hunger too long unfulfilled, a desire that could no longer be contained.

Urgently, his hand moved beneath her, seeking and exploring the firm roundness of her buttocks, lifting and pressing her into the hardness of his pelvis. Every fiber within her flamed. The weight of his chest crushed her breasts and she could hardly breathe. Yet through the hazy, aching throb of mindless desire a small amount of reason persisted, a dim fear. Always before with him she had felt protected and secure, even when her own passion threatened to sweep her out beyond her depths, because always before he had been in control. Gentle, thoughtful, he had always maintained some measure of restraint no matter how urgent his own need was, because he had cared about what became of both of them. What flamed between them now had begun in violence, no matter that it had turned to a genuine passion later, and all restraints were cast aside. It wasn't right. She did not want him like this, without tenderness or compassion or genuine emotion, only two bodies interacting with one another. It wasn't right.

His hand moved impatiently along her bare back and then to the band of material at her neck, seeking a zipper or a clasp. "Damn," he muttered huskily against her cheek. "I think you women design these outfits purely to torment a man. How do you get out of this thing?"

Some amount of reason filtered through at that, alarm coupled with desperation. She pushed weakly at him with her free hand; the other hand had grown numb beneath the ruthless grip of his fingers about her wrist which he, as well as she, had ignored until now.

"No," she insisted, turning her head. Her lips felt heavy and her voice was unsteady, it came out as nothing more than a weak plea. "Don't—not now. Please, stop."

"No." There was a viciousness in his voice as his mouth sought hers again. "You've tortured me long enough. I'm going to get you out of my system once and for all."

If he had intended to, he could not have said anything more efficiently designed to cool her mounting passion. The statement, crude and thoughtless and totally without human emotion, penetrated the fiery haze of desire and left her cold. It was an abrupt, painful, empty sensation, it brought the ache of tears to her throat and a furious demand to her voice.

"No!" She found the strength in her muscles to struggle against him, even though the effort left her shaking. "I said stop it! I don't want—" She pushed hard at his face with her fingers. "You're hurting me—let me go!"

Something in her tone reached him, penetrating the fog of passion in his eyes and, for just a moment, leaving them confused. But quickly that uncertainty disappeared and was replaced by a deep gleam of something so hateful she could not look at it; she turned away. He sat up, pulling her with him with an increased pressure on her arm, and he spat viciously, "What's the matter? Did I take you by surprise? Aren't your reporters in place, your photographers ready to leap out and capture our connubial bliss forever on film? Or did you just lose your courage?"

Abruptly, he released her wrist. She gave a little gasp of pain, both physical and emotional, and automatically began to rub her arm against the tingling sensation of returning circulation. There were red marks on the white flesh where his fingers had gripped so ruthlesly. Her eyes were brimming with confusion and hurt and her breath was coming in uneven, shallow gasps. Her voice was tight and high, and she could barely form intelligible words.

"W-what are you talking about?" she demanded shakily. "What is wrong with you? How—how could you..."

He turned away with a short, hissed oath, running his fingers through his hair, bitterness and anger radiating from every muscle of his body. It was more than just sexual frustration, more, even, than anger with her. The tight lines of his lips and his flared nostrils reflected fury—with himself and with a situation over which he no longer had control—and, perhaps, below the surface, a small bit of shame. He reached for the pack of cigarettes on the table with a curt motion, and she stood unsteadily.

She did not know what to do, or what to think. Her senses still throbbed and confusion had knotted into a hard lump in the pit of her stomach. She wanted so desperately to reach him, to understand what was going on inside him, but the shield he had thrown up against her was like a wall of ice. The only thing she could think to do was to move away from him, to give him space and give them both a chance to recover themselves, and she had to do it quickly because she was afraid she was going to burst into tears at any moment.

She went into the kitchen, not really knowing why, just moving automatically into gestures of normalcy. Her legs were wobbly and she was not thinking clearly; she bumped into the kitchen table but hardly felt the bruise. She opened a cabinet automatically, vaguely thinking something about the coffee, and she saw him stand and fling the pack of cigarettes back onto the table without lighting one.

When he spoke, some of the blind fury had gone out of his voice, but it was still heavily edged with bitterness, and the challenge could not be ignored.

"Well, now you've seen me at my worst," he said, not looking at her. "What will you do, go to the press with an account of my ruthless temper and uncontrollable base instincts? Or better yet, file charges. Attempted rape and aggravated assault. Believe me, you have a damn good case."

Her shaking hands overturned a water glass; it tumbled into the sink with a sharp crashing sound, spraying broken glass all over the counter. But she hardly noticed it. She whirled on him in shock and horror, and saw, behind the uneasiness in his eyes, genuine accusation there.

"How—how dare you!" she cried. Her voice broke into a breathless gasp, but she plunged on, the wild hurt which flamed inside her giving her courage when all she really wanted to do was run away and hide from this man who was masquerading as Trey. "How can you think I would—how could you *say* such a thing?"

The tears spilled over, blurring his face, and she turned away blindly, gathering up the pieces of broken glass with shaking fingers. "You have no right—whatever is bothering you, you shouldn't take it out on me.... It isn't like you to take it out on me!" In her carelessness, a sharp piece of glass slipped from her hand; she saw a long cut appear on her forefinger. She stared at it, not feeling the pain, and the anger and the confusion drained slowly into despair. "Oh, Trey..." Her voice broke, but the tears no longer threatened.

She turned to him, and all that she felt for him was in her eyes. He was hurting and he was closing her out when all she wanted to do was comfort him and share his pain.

"Why won't you talk to me?" she pleaded. "We can share it, whatever is bothering you. It doesn't have to be like this. You know I want to help you, but I can't if you don't tell me what's wrong."

She saw something flicker over his expression—a softening, caution combined with the need to believe her. And then he lowered his eyes briefly. When he looked up again all he said was, "Your hand is bleeding."

"It's just a scratch," she murmured quickly and turned unsteadily to attend to it. She reached for a paper towel, but her shaking hand dislodged the entire roll. It tumbled over the counter and onto the floor, and she simply stared at it, feeling drained and empty and helpless.

He was beside her, taking her injured hand between his strong and competent fingers, holding it beneath the flow of cold water. He found the package of emergency bandages she kept in a drawer and attended to the cut with swift, silent efficiency. She tried to relax beneath the ministrations of his hands, which were no longer rough yet not quite gentle, but all she was really aware of was that his touch was impersonal, his stance beside her stiff. She ached to reach out and touch him, but still he kept that cautious shield between them. She felt as though she had lost something unaccountably precious, and the worst of it was that she did not know why. The sorrow of the loss and confusion throbbed bitterly inside her.

When he looked at her, the anger was gone. There was weariness in his eyes, and regret on his face. He said quietly, "You look pale. Maybe you'd better sit down."

She shook her head numbly. If she were pale, it was not due to a minor cut on her finger, and she was too tense to sit down. A thousand questions were whirling within her, and she had the answers to none of them. She took a step away from him, her hands clasped rigidly before her, and wondered only what was going to happen next.

Then she felt his hand very lightly on her shoulder. His touch, even after all that had happened and all that was left unanswered, still had the power to start a quiver of anticipation inside her, to drain away the hurt into a sharper, more acute longing.

He said quietly, "I'm sorry I acted like a sex-starved adolescent before. I've never ..." He broke off with a soft sigh.

She turned to look at him. Her eyes were still wide with anxiety and the aftereffects of shock, and filled with a silent plea. If only he would do or say something, anything, to make it all right between them again. She did not even care why it had happened any longer, if only he would put his arms about her and she could feel tenderness from him again. But all she saw in his eyes was sorrow.

"You really have seen the worst of me," he said. He tried to smile and failed. He lowered his eyes. "I don't usually lose my temper, in the boardroom or the bedroom. No one has ever been able to do that to me before. I suppose... because no one has ever mattered so much to me before."

Immediately as the words were spoken he looked as though he regretted them, and the hope which flared within her was just as quickly extinguished. She felt the stiffening of his body next to hers; he dropped his hand from her shoulder. When he did smile, it came nowhere near reaching his eyes, and he said simply, "I'll say good night before I do any more damage."

She could do nothing but helplessly watch him cross the room, wanting to call out for him but not knowing what to say. At the door he stopped to pick up his jacket, and then he turned back. She was certain then he would return; the longing and the regret on his face wrenched at her heart. But he said nothing, and in another moment he was gone.

THROUGHOUT THE NIGHT she lay wide-eyed and aching, trying to somehow resign herself to what had happened. *You never knew him,* a secret, awed voice kept whispering inside her. *You threw yourself into this relationship without thinking twice and you never really knew the man.... It was all an illusion.* Trey had been right, Art had been right, all those people who had warned her repeatedly to proceed with caution had been right all along. She had flung herself headlong into one impulsive adventure too many, and the raw, unsalvable pain she was feeling now was the result. She had allowed herself to fall in love with a man she did not even know.

Love. Was that what it was? How could it be any-

thing else and hurt so badly? *But no one falls in love in
two weeks,* the newly formed, sensible side of herself
counseled her. *Not really. How can you love a stranger?*

But, with a soft moan of despair, she knew that was
exactly what she had done. Because she did not believe
Trey was really a stranger, she knew that somewhere
just below the surface was the man she had grown to
care about more than anyone she had ever cared for in
her life, and that even as he tried to push her away he
only drew her closer . . . that she would never, ever, be
the same without him.

"Oh, God," she whispered tremulously to the darkened ceiling, blinking back tears, "what a mess."

She brought her hands to her face, pushing back her
hair, biting her lip, trying to think rationally. She tried
to tell herself it was probably all for the best. It would
never work out. How could she love a man she was
sworn to defeat? How could she care for him when it
was her duty to crush his dreams and sweep away his
career? Her loyalty was to Addison Cantrell; she truly
believed he was the best candidate, and her only destiny was to see him in Washington with herself by his
side. This was her one chance at a lifelong dream and
she could not risk it with foolish emotions and unat-
tainable desires.

Be sensible for once in your life, Lindsey, she told herself sternly. *It would never work out. He's leaving tomorrow and what happened tonight—for whatever reasons—
was for the best. Don't torture yourself with crazy yearn-
ings. Let it go.*

But she could not. Because somewhere deep down
inside, she still believed in him.

After a tortured and restless night, nothing was
clearer in the morning. She dressed for work numbly,

dreading the day ahead, dreading all the long and empty days ahead without Trey.

When the telephone rang, her heart began to thump before she even answered it. She was not sure whether the sudden tightening in her throat was from anticipation or trepidation, and her voice was timid and uncertain as she picked up the receiver.

Trey sounded tired, reserved, and a little anxious. He asked, "Could I see you today?"

She hesitated. Something far away advised her: *Caution, caution*..."I have to work today," she answered.

"It's Saturday."

"I know, but...my job isn't always five days a week." There was a silence, and she wanted to take back her refusal immediately. Instead she found herself saying, "I thought you were leaving today."

"I didn't want to leave without telling you"—he seemed to hesitate over the word—"good-bye." He sighed. "I didn't want to leave things as they were last night. But I don't blame you for not wanting to see me." His voice was heavy. She knew he was about to say good-bye, and her fingers tightened on the telephone.

She did not think about it twice. "I'll be ready in fifteen minutes," she said softly.

It did not occur to her until much later that she had just made her first conscious decision between Addison Cantrell and Trey Sinclair.

Trey was casually dressed, impeccably groomed, but his face looked haggard. Immediately her heart went out to him as she saw him, and everything of the night before was wiped away. All she wanted to do was erase that haunted look from his face.

She greeted him with a bright smile. "Do you want

to come in, or are we going someplace? Do I need my purse?"

"Your keys," he reminded her.

She reached for her purse from the coatrack, and she heard his soft intake of breath behind her. As she turned, he reached for her arm, slowly turning it to reveal three pale blue bruises on the soft white underside of her wrist. He looked at it for a long time, and she saw the muscles of his jaw tighten, his lips compressed grimly. He said lowly, "Did I do that?"

She retrieved her arm quickly. "I bruise easily," she assured him matter-of-factly. "All fair-skinned people do."

He was silent as they walked to his car, and a pall seemed to hang over them which was reflected in the high white cloud cover which washed over the sky in silver-gray and muted the sun. When he had made the turn onto the expressway, Lindsey looked at him and commented gently, "I think the stress of the campaign is beginning to tell on you. You have dark circles under your eyes."

"There's a simpler explanation for that," he replied, his eyes on the road. "I didn't go to bed until four o'clock and then I didn't sleep."

She moved her eyes away from the weary, tormented lines of his face. She did not know what to say or how to reach him. She told herself that it was enough, for the moment, that she was with him, and that there was still a chance.

He took her to Sweetwater Creek, a small day-use park west of Atlanta. There were no other cars in the parking lot as they pulled up. "This is kind of a secret place for me," he told her, and it was the first sentence he had spoken in the past half hour. "There usually aren't many people here; I guess the place is not very well known. It looks like we have it all to ourselves this morning."

He extended his hand to her as he opened her door. "I thought we would just walk awhile," he explained. "There are miles of hiking trails. Sometimes just walking along them helps me think."

She placed her hand within his and accepted his unspoken request for silence. He held her hand as he guided her toward a wooded path.

They walked along the course of a lazily winding creek, and Lindsey let herself become absorbed in the silence and natural beauty. It *was* a secret place, and the dim overcast sky and the cool breeze sealed them off in a world of their own, of shared silence and undemanding companionship. The wide, still water stretched smoothly between tree-shrouded banks, its silver flow interrupted at intervals by flat yellow sandbars. There was no sound but the crunch of their steps on the pinestraw and the scurrying of small animals, and very far away, so rhythmic and musical it almost blended completely into the background, was a muted roar, as though of a heavy wind or rushing water. Lindsey knew the sound could not be generated by the still beauty of the creek by which they now walked, but she did not wonder over it unduly. The sound was hypnotic, the peaceful day wrapped itself about them, and Trey's hand was warm and strong about hers. As they walked, she felt the tension slide from him as it did from her, and she loved him for bringing her to this place, for sharing this with her.

As they continued along the trail, the muted roar became louder, a throbbing pulse-beat which seemed to blend into the taste of the cool, fresh air and become a part of all that surrounded them. Rounding a corner, Lindsey gave an exclamation of delight as the placid stream suddenly burst into a roaring river, dashing itself against rocks and spilling over shoals, churning and whirling in gushes of white water as far as the eye could see. She stood transfixed, trying to take it all in at once.

"It's something, isn't it?" agreed Trey. "I think this is my favorite part of the park. Something about all that power has a way of putting things into perspective."

She smiled at him, her eyes shining, and stepped toward the edge. "Be careful," he cautioned, but he released her hand and let her go.

Smooth flat rocks provided perfect stepping-stones across whirlpools of foamy water, and she made her way to one large boulder in the center which was worn smooth and glassy in places by centuries of the rushing water's enormous energy, but was still firm enough to provide a secure foothold. She climbed on top and sat down, her arms clasped about her knees, surrounded on all sides by magnificent sound and throbbing energy, and she let all her cares drift away into the foaming water.

She did not know how long she stayed there. It might have been an hour, it might have been only a few minutes. The constant pounding and spray of the water had a mesmerizing effect; she let her mind go completely blank in response to it. She thought nothing, she worried about nothing, she felt nothing except an overwhelming peace and confidence in the future. Trey had brought her here, to his special place, as though knowing without being told that what she needed most was an opportunity to relax and put things in perspective, to put her own thoughts together and regain an uncomplicated view on matters. It was as though in satisfying his own needs, he had satisfied hers as well, and she had never felt closer to anyone, more a part of anyone, than she did to him at that moment.

At last she looked up, and Trey was still standing on the bank, his eyes directed toward the cascading falls downstream, lost in his own thoughts, dreaming his own dreams. She got up and made her way carefully back to him, slipping her hand into his and smiling up at him. She said simply, "Thank you."

He smiled at her, and for the first time in over twenty-four hours, all she saw in his eyes was clear welcome. He slipped his arm about her waist as they began walking again. "Over a hundred years ago," he said, "this entire area was a bustling industrial town called New Manchester."

She looked up at him in surprise. "You mean this is a ghost town?"

He nodded. "It employed over two hundred people at the mill, most of whom lived in little company-owned houses right where we're walking. During the Civil War it supplied cloth for uniforms and tents for the Confederate Army."

She looked up at him, fascinated. "What happened?"

"Naturally, it became an important Union military target. On Sherman's march to the sea, over four hundred people from Sweetwater and Roswell were rounded up and herded like cattle, on foot, to Marietta, about twenty miles away. There they were shipped up North to prison camps—men, women, and children. The factory was burned, and most of the town, too, I imagine. If anyone ever came back, they didn't find much to stay for. New Manchester was abandoned, and soon forgotten. Sometimes," he added softly, "when it's very quiet, on days like this, I imagine I can hear the voices of all those people, the ghosts of those who were torn away from their homes and the only life they had ever known...." And he smiled at her, gently and contemplatively. "And sometimes, I think it's nothing more than the ghosts of my own thoughts."

She loved him then, with a power and a certainty which washed over her completely and left her weak. She loved him for the poet and the dreamer, the idealist who had seen his ideals crushed but who had survived all the stronger for it; she loved his wit and his charm and his sensitivity, his honesty and his pragmatism. She loved the dark eyes and the wavy hair and the aquiline nose, and nothing else mattered except she loved him, all of him, and he was beside her.

She stopped and turned to him, slipping her arms about his waist and reaching her hands up to press his shoulders. His face moved toward hers slowly as she lifted hers to him, and he took her lips very gently, almost hesitantly, as though expecting her to draw away. But she did not. She tightened her arms about him and returned his kiss joyfully, letting herself be carried away by the warmth of his body enfolding hers and the roar of the water sealing them off into an exclusive, timeless world where nothing existed except the dizzying, electrifying kiss of the man she loved.

He held her tightly, his breath a warm stream against her neck, and she could feel the thudding of his heart against her breast and the barely perceptible quivering of his muscles beneath her fingers. He whispered, "Lindsey..."

"Don't," she protested, for she knew very well what he was going to say.

"I have to." He took her shoulders and pushed her a little away, and the expression on his face for just that moment was pure torment. He cleared it with a breath, though, and when he spoke there was only regret in his eyes, deep with sincerity. "I want you to know that last night—it wasn't me. I was angry about something that really had nothing to do with you..." He dropped his eyes briefly, shielding whatever might have been revealed there. "I suppose," he admitted, "I was really angry with myself. I had to do some hard thinking, and re-examine my priorities, and put some things in perspective. I think I've done that."

She nodded, not really understanding, but accepting it because he asked her to.

He smiled a little, and inquired softly, "Forgive me?"

She answered steadily, "There was never anything to forgive."

"Oh, Lindsey..." It was hardly more than a breath, and his eyes closed slowly, as though against a great pain. The kiss he placed on her forehead was very light, very gentle, and he whispered, "You've brought magic into my life. Whatever happens, that was worth it all."

Pleasure overwhelmed her, and love, but also confusion. But before she could speak, he dropped his arm to her waist and began walking again. When next he spoke his tone was conversational, and the moment for questions and confessions had passed. "I want you to do me a favor while I'm gone," he said.

That brought back with devastating newness the reality of his leaving, and she determinedly fought back the ache within her. She did not want him to go, not when she had only just discovered how much of her life was wrapped up in him. But she could not ask him to stay, she told herself sensibly, and it wouldn't be forever.... She managed brightly, "What?"

He reached into his pocket and took out his keys. "Water my plants," he told her.

She took the keys from him with a nervous little laugh. "The keys to your house—I'm honored! Are you sure you trust me enough?"

He leaned forward and kissed her lips very gently. "I think so," he answered.

The sobriety in his voice, the quiet strength of his gentle touch caused a flutter of pleasure to go through her, and also a measure of confusion. She brought her eyes to him in question, but, again, the moment was gone. "Also," he added lightly, reaching into his pocket again and producing a piece of paper with a flourish, "a map. Guaranteed to get you from your house to mine without undue incident—provided, of course, that you follow the instructions explicitly."

She took it from him and unfolded it. It was a detailed drawing of the route between their two residences with colorful written instructions such as, "Stop sign—brake fully," "Yield to oncoming traffic," "Signal and change lanes," and "upon completion of journey, make sure that a) gear indicator is in Park, b) ignition is off, c) headlights are off, d) seat belt is unfastened," She burst into laughter and struck at him playfully with the paper; he caught her against his chest and lifted her off the ground, and as he whirled her around the sun suddenly broke through the clouds, turning the day golden.

Chapter Eight

The following weeks were the busiest and at the same time the emptiest of Lindsey's life. She worked on Uncle Addison's campaign during the day and dreamed about Trey at night. May turned into June, and she followed Trey's progress on the campaign trail as diligently as if he had been her candidate, but from Trey himself she heard nothing.

She attended to Trey's plants scrupulously, with a consistency which would have amazed everyone who knew her for the absentminded, easily distracted person she was. Every day she went to his house, even if it were one or two o'clock in the morning before she left headquarters, opened the windows, watered the plants, and did whatever dusting or straightening that was required. She gave much more attention to his possessions than she did her own, and when she left she always made sure the doors and windows were locked and the porch light was on. Sometimes, when she felt the need to escape from the pressures of the day, she would open the glass cabinet and examine his animal miniatures, feeling close to him by touching the things he treasured.

One Saturday afternoon when she was so involved, she was startled by the sound of tires on the driveway.

Her heart leaped to her throat in a jolt of happiness and anticipation, and she thought, *Trey!* For a moment she could not even move, but when at last she ran to the window it was only to be disappointed. It was not Trey, but his mother, who was getting out of a long white car and coming up the walk.

For a moment her disappointment was so acute it obscured everything else, but then she heard the click of high heels on the steps and a bolt of alarm went through her. What would Trey's mother think to find her here? She was pretty sure Trey had not bothered to tell his mother that Lindsey had a key to the house, and this could be very embarrassing.

She squared her shoulders determinedly and went to the door, opening it just as Irene MacDonald was preparing to insert her key.

"Why, Lindsey!" she exclaimed, obviously pleased. "How nice!"

Warming to the fact that Trey's mother did not seem to be in the least taken aback by finding a stranger in her son's house, and that, in fact, she even seemed happy about it, Lindsey relaxed. "Mrs. MacDonald," she said, stepping back with a smile. "How nice to see you again. I—I'm surprised you remembered me."

The other woman laughed, stepping inside. "Now really, dear, you don't imagine my son brings home so many girls that I forget their names! No, indeed, meeting you was a rare and special event, and I wouldn't be so bad a parent as to forget. And," she beamed, "I insist you call me Irene. Are you living here now, dear?"

Lindsey was taken aback, as much by the question as by Irene's casual delivery of it. "N-no," she stammered. "I...just come by to water the plants while Trey is away."

"Now, isn't that silly," commented Irene, moving about the room. Lindsey assumed she was referring to the living arrangements. "But Trey was always concerned with all that's right and proper, which, I suppose, is what makes him a perfect stuffed-shirt politician."

Lindsey could not help giggling at the image of Trey as a "stuffed shirt," and Irene smiled at her.

"I only came by to check on the house," she went on. "I suppose I should have done it sooner, but I've been so busy.... It's just as well he made other arrangements, isn't it? I do think, though," she added meaningfully, "it would be much simpler if you just moved in. You be sure to speak to him about that, dear."

Lindsey suppressed another giggle at the endearing presumption of the woman, but no response was required, for Irene began moving about the room, examining walls and draperies and ceiling beams with an air of approval. "I sold Trey this house, did you know that? He's kept it up well. I knew it would be perfect for him."

Her eyes fell on the open cabinet of miniatures, and she went over to it, exclaiming, "Oh, I see he's added a few pieces! I don't get over here very often," she confessed. "He has a glass deer I have been begging him for for ages. I wonder what would happen if I just sort of slipped it into my purse now?"

"He would press charges, probably," laughed Lindsey, joining her at the cabinet, and Irene smiled.

"I think you're probably right, dear. Blood is definitely not thicker than water when it comes to Trey's interpretation of the law."

She picked up a few pieces, exclaiming over her favorites, replacing them carefully on the shelf; Lindsey pointed out her favorites and soon they were involved in a discussion of art. It was revealed that Lindsey's father was a sculptor.

"Madison," murmured Irene, her pretty brow creasing in thoughtfulness. "You wouldn't by any remote chance happen to be related to Daniel Madison?"

"He's my father," confessed Lindsey, pleased.

Irene's eyes flew open in delighted surprise. "Now, you don't say! Do you know, my dear, I believe I am one of the few people still living who has actually met the man? That old hermit! We ran into each other at a bohemian beach party—oh, years back—now, don't look so shocked, my dear, he may be your father but he's got a little life left in him yet. And as for me"—her smile was secretly superior—"I've been around." She laughed softly, lost in remembering. "My, we had one high night, that we did. What a character." And then her eyes returned to Lindsey, bright with excitement and pleasure. "I'm an avid collector of his work, you know—which is to say, I probably own as many of his pieces as anyone in the Free World. You must come and see them sometime." She took her arm companionably and led her to the sofa. "What's he up to these days?"

"Oh, immersed in his newest masterpiece, as usual," replied Lindsey. "Happy as a clam. I wanted to see him this summer, but I've been so busy...maybe in the fall." *After the election,* she thought, and her spirits were suddenly dampened. She did not want to think about the election in the presence of Trey's mother; it was almost a betrayal.

"Well, well," sighed Irene, drawing Lindsey onto the sofa beside her. "Imagine that. My Trey and Daniel Madison's daughter. Who could have thought it?" And then she smiled. "What have you heard from my son?"

Lindsey dropped her eyes and shook her head slowly, for there was no way to try to hide the depression which was creeping over her. It had been over six weeks and Trey had not called her once. The significance of that was something she tried desperately to avoid thinking about.

Irene patted her hand lightly and reassuringly. "It's rude, I know, but Trey doesn't like to be distracted when he's campaigning. He hasn't called me, either."

Lindsey tried to smile, but it came out rather wan.

"Lindsey..." Irene's eyes were tender, full of understanding and sincerity. Lindsey was reminded poignantly of Trey. "You may think I'm a very foolish woman..." Lindsey tried to protest but she went on, "Trey and I don't see a great deal of one another, you understand, we both lead our own lives, but we have a special relationship. We've developed a way of communicating with one another almost without the use of words; I can tell by a glance, or a gesture, or the tone of his voice, what he is thinking and what he is feeling. Believe me, dear, when I tell you he cares for you a great deal. You have caused a change in him, something I've waited for all my life and never expected to see." She smiled. "It is perhaps something only a mother *can* see—when she suspects grandchildren in the future." She sighed. "I *do* so want grandchildren. You will be patient with him, won't you, dear? You won't disappoint me?"

Lindsey's laugh was of pure warmth toward the woman who, like Trey, had so quickly made her way into her heart. For the first time in weeks, she felt like looking into the future herself. Surely Trey would call her soon. They had parted on good terms, it would have been so much worse if the fight they had had the night before he left had not been resolved, and it

wasn't as though she would never see him again....
After all, he *had* to come back to collect his keys. But it
was hard to keep her spirits up for more than a moment, and soon she began to fret again. Why *hadn't* he
called her? Was there some message in his silence she
was refusing to see? Did he already regret his apology
on their last day together, or was this his gentle way of
showing her his lack of interest? He had told her,
hadn't he, that he did not have time for involvements?
And perhaps this was his way of bringing home the
truth of it. Yet how much time could a phone call take?
He could surely have called her...if he had wanted to.

A shadowy depression fell over her of the type that
had become more frequent lately. She must have been
crazy to have ever thought it would work out between
them. Even in the best of circumstances, no one could
expect to conduct a love affair in the midst of a hot
political campaign. And this... She looked at Trey's
mother, and her struggle against the pain which was
gnawing at her was clearly written in her eyes. She was
suddenly moved by a compulsion to confess everything
to this warm, kind woman. After all, Trey would have
to know sometime—she could no longer deceive herself about that—and it seemed as good a place as any to
begin with Trey's mother. She did not know how much
longer she could carry this burden by herself.

But Irene MacDonald did not give her a chance. Her
face softened at the obvious unhappiness in Lindsey's
eyes, and she said gently, "You *do* love him, don't you,
dear?"

Lindsey dropped her eyes miserably. She just couldn't.
She couldn't confess to Trey's mother that she loved
him in one breath, and that she had betrayed him in the
other. She twisted her hands together tightly, and she
said simply, very softly, "Yes. I love him."

But the question was, did he love her? And if he did, was it enough to forgive the awful crime she had committed against him? No, she decided in utter desolation, no one loved that much. She could never expect him to forgive her deception when he hated a lie above all things. They were doomed before they even started, they had no future, but she could not let him go. She did not know what to do.

Irene slipped her arm about Lindsey's shoulders and squeezed briefly and affectionately. "Well," she said, with simple confidence, "that's all that matters, isn't it? Don't look so worried, dear, everything will be all right. I'm sure of it."

Something in the woman's unquestioning certainty reached Lindsey, for she wanted so badly to believe it. Surely, she tried to tell herself, things couldn't be as bad as she imagined. Trey *did* care for her, she was certain, or else why would he have made such an effort to leave on good terms with her? And as long as he cared, just a little, it would buy them time.... And time was all she could ask for now. If only she could postpone telling him a little at a time, day by day, perhaps by the time came when the truth was no longer avoidable it wouldn't matter any more.

After all, she thought, trying to hold on to courage with a dim hope, he might not even win the primary.

ON A FRIDAY EVENING two weeks later, Lindsey let herself wearily into her apartment, fumbling for the light. She had left headquarters at seven, which was early for her, and had stopped to have a hamburger on the way home, but she had been too exhausted even to eat. She was looking forward to a long hot bath and twelve hours' sleep.

The room sprang into light and a man's voice

drawled, "I see you're still leaving your door unlocked."

She gave a little cry and dropped her purse, spilling keys and change and cosmetics all over the carpet. Trey rose lazily from the sofa, and she stared at him, blinking hard, trying to assure herself it wasn't a ghost. At last she managed, hardly above a whisper, "T-Trey!"

"Fortunately for you, I might add," he said, coming toward her easily. It might have been less than a day since he had been here, rather than almost two months.

"But—but," she stammered, still hardly able to believe it, "what are you doing here?"

"Waiting for you," he answered. "And," he confessed, "napping, but mostly escaping from my bodyguards."

He took her hands, his clasp warm and strong, and for the first time it swept over her that he was really here—his familiar scent, his warm touch, his lazy half-smile. Happiness rushed through her and left her weak, but she could only repeat stupidly, "Bodyguards?"

"They don't call themselves that," he admitted, "but I know that's what they are. I haven't had a moment to myself in eight weeks, and your place seemed like as good a refuge as any." And then his hands tightened slightly on hers, his smile became deeper.

He inquired softly, "Do I still know you well enough to kiss you?"

She nodded wordlessly and stepped into his arms.

From that moment the dreariness and emptiness of the past weeks evaporated as though it had never been. The familiar soaring ecstasy swept over her in the softness of his lips, the firm pressure of his fingers against her back, the hard length of his body. Her fingers found the exquisite silky texture of his hair and she separated the strands, ran her fingers through it, explored the strong column of his neck, and gave herself over completely to the warm, dizzy wonder of being in his arms again. There was no mistaking what they shared in that kiss—nothing had been lost between them, it was all as it had been from the beginning, and her happiness was so complete it almost brought tears to her eyes.

When he looked down at her there was tenderness in his eyes, a smile of warmth and welcome on his lips, and his hands caressed her waist through the material of her sheer summer dress with barely restrained eagerness. But he said simply, "You haven't changed a bit you know." And he stepped back, dropping his gaze to her feet.

She followed the direction of his eyes in some confusion, and as she stepped away, she saw what he meant. A tube of lipstick, crushed beneath her shoe, had broken open and the gorgeous peach color was ground into her white carpet. She made a soft sound of despair and bent to pick it up just as he did, missing a collision by inches. He sat back on his heels, his eyes snapping with laughter, and her spirits soared to see him like that again.

"God, I've missed you!" he exclaimed.

She dropped her eyes quickly, hurriedly scooping up the spilled contents of her purse, and tried to make her voice casual as she asked, "Then why didn't you call me?"

She missed the expression on his face, but there was no mistaking a subtle change in his tone as he answered, "I had my reasons." Then he held out her purse for her, and as she dumped the contents back inside there was nothing in his eyes but impatience, thinly disguised restlessness, and eagerness to be away.

He pulled her to her feet, and, to her surprise, turned and took her overnight bag from the chair near the door. His hand on her elbow was possessive and insistent, and all he said was, "Come along."

She stared at him and at the bag in his hand. "Come where? What's that?"

"Just a few things you'll need for the weekend."

She continued to stare as he half-led, half-pushed her out the door. So many questions were clamoring to be answered that she could only stammer, "You—you *packed* for me?"

His smile in the pale twilight was tolerantly amused. "Come on, Lindsey, this is the twentieth century, don't look so shocked. I do know a little about what goes on over the female body, and anything I forgot you'll just have to do without. Time is of the essence."

She relapsed into stunned silence as she was bundled into his car, the door securely closed and locked, and he came around quickly to the other side. The weekend, she realized suddenly. He had said the weekend. All she had dreamed for, and all, it occurred to her in a jolt of reality, she had every reason to try desperately to avoid. The time she had hoped for and prayed for was swiftly running out, for how could she spend a weekend with him, loving him, wanting him, knowing she was deceiving him? This was not how she had planned it at all.

"Trey," she began a little desperately, turning to him as he backed out of the parking space, "we can't do this! I mean, we can't just take off—you have responsibilities...."

"Which," he responded easily, "I intend to blissfully ignore for the next two days." He turned on to the street.

"But..." She cast about in her mind frantically for

some way to dissuade him, and then she found herself blurting, "What if the opposition found out? I know sex-scandals are a little old-fashioned but they *do* still happen, and what if someone found out that you disappeared for the weekend with a girl you weren't married to? Think of the consequences!"

There was a very brief silence. Then he said, carefully, "I don't think anyone will find out. And if they did, I imagine I would survive it."

She shook her head determinedly, for a moment forgetting entirely who she was and who she was working for, concerned only about him. "No. Your personal life is your most vulnerable area. Being young and single, and because no one can find anything else wrong with you, you have to guard your moral image very carefully. Don't you know the press is ready to rip you to shreds at the slightest infraction? You can't afford to slip, Trey, you don't realize—"

"Sometimes you have to take chances, Lindsey," he interrupted quietly. He pulled up to a stop sign and turned to her. His expression in the dark was completely unreadable—it could have been challenge, it could have been tenderness—but the tone of his voice was unmistakably serious. "If you can tell me truthfully that you don't want to go, if you can look at me now and tell me you don't want to be with me this weekend, then we'll turn back. But that's the only thing that's going to change my mind."

If only he had not put it like that. How could she lie to him when the truth was written all over her face—that all she wanted forever was to be with him? *No,* she thought miserably, sinking back into her seat, *you can't lie to him about that but you can lie to him about everything else.* She said nothing.

Exit signs and billboards, county borders and city

limits flew past as they drove through the night, and Lindsey began to relax against the hypnotic purr of the engine and the familiar comfort of his presence. As always, it was easy for her to push the problems aside for just another minute, to tell herself that everything was going to be all right one more time, to avoid, for the present, looking into the face of reality.

At last she stirred herself to inquire, "Where are we going, anyway?"

"Newnan," he answered. "It's not very far—we're almost there. Have you ever been?"

She shook her head. Until she had begun work on the campaign, she had not even heard of it. She knew it was a small, historic town in western Georgia, a primarily agricultural community, and—

"I was raised there," Trey refreshed her memory. "On the farm."

"Farm!" She sat up straight with a little laugh. "It's more of a plantation, I hear. Why are we going there?"

"Because," he answered, "at this point in my campaign, that's the last place anyone would think of looking for me."

He turned off the expressway, and the landscape on either side dissolved into endless miles of soybeans, tall rows of corn, swaying alfalfa. One enormous field was planted in nothing but shrubs; another stretched forever in cotton. She strained her eyes in all directions, trying to take in all of the silent beauty which surrounded her.

If she had expected one of those stately old antebellum mansions, she was to be disappointed as Trey turned into a driveway and the headlights flashed on the dark windows of a modern brick ranch-style house. "Is this yours?" she asked, surprised.

"My cousins'," he answered. "All the farm business

is managed by one group of cousins or the other, now.''

Of course, she had known that. And just as she was thinking with a cautious mixture of relief and disappointment that they were not going to be completely alone, after all, he opened her door and informed her, ''They're out of town now.''

She stepped out into the warm night air, inhaling the rich fragrance of magnolia and new-mown hay, absorbing the stillness. The canopy of endless, glittering bright stars was almost three-dimensional, and the chirping of the crickets was so loud it sounded like an orchestra.

But as Trey inserted his key into the lock the old trepidation crept over her again, and she ventured, ''Are you sure it's okay? I mean, won't your cousins mind our being here?''

''No, I've done it before.'' He glanced at her with a grin. ''Previously alone,'' he specified. ''They've told me many times I'm welcome to use the house when they're away.''

She hesitated as he swung open the door and turned on an inner light. She felt as though if she stepped over that threshold she would be irretrievably committed to a decision she was not certain she was ready to make yet. ''But they could come back...''

He drew her inside with a hand firmly on her arm. ''They're in Puerto Rico,'' he told her. ''They're not due back for another month.''

She said in a small voice, ''Oh.'' And lowered her overnight bag and her purse slowly to the floor.

He crossed the room, switching on lamps, telling her, ''The freezer is stocked, and there are fresh vegetables in the garden, and we can get milk from the dairy. We'll be all right here a couple of days. The bedroom"—he opened a door for her—"is here. You can put your things away if you like. I'm going to take a shower."

When he left, she sank to the black leather sofa, releasing her breath slowly and cautiously. She told herself she was being silly. This was what she wanted, wasn't it?—to be with the man she loved, alone for the entire weekend? This did not change anything; she was still working for Addison Cantrell and she still loved Trey Sinclair; the situation was just as it had been for the past three months and she had somehow managed to live with it. Why should she suddenly be so nervous?

She was so wrapped up in her own consternation that she did not hear him come in, and she jumped as she felt a light brush of fingers across the back of her neck, and then the warm clasp of lips. She twisted around, startled. "Trey!"

His eyes crinkled as he came around the sofa to sit beside her. "Who were you expecting?"

He was wearing a brown velour robe which fell to just above his knees and opened to reveal a thin triangle of bare chest covered with a light mat of dark hair, and she was pretty certain he was wearing nothing under it. Only seeing him like that, knowing that they had never been this close before, sent a little shiver of anticipation through her. Unfortunately, it was translated into nervousness as he sat beside her and rested her arm across the back of the sofa, his fingers caressing her shoulder. She said brightly, "So. How's the campaign going?"

There was amusement on his face but something deeper in his eyes as they searched her face, flickered over the swell of her bosom and the bare flesh of her neck and chest revealed by the modest square neckline of her voile dress. He answered negligently, "Don't you read the papers? It's going very well. They're saying I'm a sure bet for the primary."

She swallowed hard against the slow tightening of the muscles of her abdomen. Even his glance could do that to her; no more than a light touch of his fingers on her shoulder... She said, managing a little laugh, "You haven't asked about your plants."

His eyes rested on her lips, and there was nothing there to suggest he was even remotely interested in plants. "Still alive and well?"

She nodded wordlessly, and just when she thought he would close the distance between them with his lips, he smiled, tenderly and affectionately. His hand stroked her hair, once, and then rested on the back of the sofa. "You don't have to be nervous, you know," he said gently.

"I-I'm not nervous," she tried to protest, but even as she spoke she was inching away from him.

"Lindsey." The tone of his voice was patient but insistent, full of understanding and demanding no less than honesty.

She dropped her eyes to her tightly entwined fingers. "Well," she admitted, "maybe a little. You...took me by surprise...." How could she tell him the real reason for her nervousness? How *could* she?

"I know," he admitted. "I warned you, didn't I, that you couldn't have come into my life at a worse time? We have to snatch our moments where we can."

"I understand that," she said softly, not looking at him.

He lifted her chin gently with his finger, forcing her to meet his eyes. There was nothing but sincerity there. He said, "I want you to know that I didn't stop thinking about you once in all these weeks. I dreamed about you. And no matter how hard I tried to forget about you, I couldn't. All I could think about was coming back here, having you in my arms again..." For the briefest moment, he dropped his eyes. "That's why I didn't call you," he admitted, looking at her again. "I was afraid if I heard your voice nothing else would matter and I would be back here like a shot. Lindsey, no one else has ever done this to me before. It took me by surprise, I didn't know how to deal with it, and I needed the time to sort out my feelings for you."

Her breath was coming shallowly, her lips parted on an uncertain question. Her eyes searched his face desperately, for that was all she had ever wanted to hear, all she had ever needed to know.... She whispered, "Which are?"

He answered with a kiss. Her response was as uncontrollable as it was desperate. In his arms she could forget everything else, she could believe everything was going to be all right because nothing else mattered except that she loved him and she wanted him, and he was here. She wanted only to belong to him. The world revolved to the essence of the sensual experience, and she was lost to it. Her lips parted helplessly beneath the insistence of his, and the taste of his tongue was faintly peppermint. His hair was soft and fluffy beneath her fingers, still damp about the ends, and the heat of his bared chest pressed into her breasts, generating within her a whole new set of unexpected emotions. Her hands were pushing back the material of his robe, exploring more of the firm broadness of his chest, and her lips were against the smooth, clean taste of his face and his neck. The quivering ache inside her mounted uncontrollably with the hot flush that seared her body and the shiver of his warm breath on her ear, and her throat, his lips pressing against the material which covered her breast. His hand caressed her stockinged knee and then slipped beneath her skirt to trace the course of her thigh upward toward her hip, and then, frustrated by the waistband, sought her back again to press her against him in one final, urgently demanding kiss.

"Lindsey," he whispered against her cheek. "Let's go to bed."

His fingers closed about hers to urge her upward, and she turned her face, depserately seeking some control over the situation and her own torrent of emotions and desires, trying to regulate her breathing into some semblance of normalcy, trying to subdue the thudding of her heart and the awful ache he had started inside her. His fingers tightened on hers as he started to stand, and with every last ounce of her strength and her courage, she pulled her hand away. "I—I can't!" she whispered brokenly.

There was a long silence. He moved his arm from about her waist and reached up to brush her hair away from her forehead, and then he inquired gently, "What's wrong?"

She looked at him, all of the agony and conflict of the past weeks reflected on her face. But in his eyes she saw only quiet encouragement beneath the steady light of desire, ready understanding, and the promise that she could tell him nothing so terrible that he would change his feelings for her. She wanted to cling to the promise in those eyes like the last ballast in a storm-tossed world...but she couldn't. Not for this. There would be no refuge from this.

She forced strength into her legs and stood abruptly, winding her hands together and walking a few steps away from him. There was no turning back now, she had to tell him. She had burned her bridges behind her and if only she could still the trembling, if only she could hold back the tears and force the words out one at a time.... Her eyes were brimming and she had to part her lips for breath, but she squared her shoulders and lifted her chin and she refused to break down. She had done nothing to be ashamed of, she had never deliberately meant this to happen, she was not ashamed of who she was or what she had chosen to do with her life.... But she kept her back to him, because she knew when next she looked at him there would be hatred in his eyes, and she wanted to remember, for as long as she could, the tenderness that had once been there.

She said tightly, "My uncle is Addison Cantrell. My brother is his campaign manager and I'm his assistant." There, all in a rush, the worst was over. She had said it, and her words echoed like a ringing anathema in the still, ominously silent room. He did not make a sound behind her, or even move, and as great as the urge was to turn to him, to see what was written on his face, hoping against hope that she would find forgiveness there, her courage failed her. She went on, desperately fighting against the trembling of her entire body, which threatened to break her voice, and against the tears, which swam with moisture in her mouth and her nose and blurred her vision.

"I didn't know who you were at first." Each word was slow and deliberate, enunciated as clearly as she could, emphasizing her desperate struggle for control. "I never meant to deliberately deceive you." There was no use pleading for him to believe her, for he would either accept her story or he would not and nothing she could say would make a difference. All she could do was to tell the truth at last, and despite the agony it was causing her, it was a relief to no longer hide. "I know I should have told you as soon as I found out, but I was afraid.... And then it was too late. I know it's stupid, but—by then—I was in love with you...." There her voice broke, but only for a moment. Two tears slipped down her cheeks, but she swallowed the lump in her throat determinedly; she lifted her chin, taking a short breath in an effort to regain control. She would not be pitied. Her pride was all she had left, and she would not beg. "I believe in Addison Cantrell for the Senate," she said fiercely, in a low rush. She clenched her hands together so tightly that the nails dug into her flesh and the fingers began to throb. "I'm going to continue to work for him and I'm going to do everything in my power to see that you're defeated in this election. And..." No more. She could not say any more. She closed her eyes and finished in almost a whisper, "That's all I have to say."

There was a long, long silence. The room practically throbbed with it, and the painful pounding of her heart and the wet sounds of her breathing were a dim counterpoint. And then he said, very quietly, "I know."

The sudden cold shock was so intense that she actually felt faint. She whirled, seeking in his face some confirmation of the words, and she found only a sober acknowledgment of the truth there. The color drained from her face as the strength drained from her legs and she sank to a chair weakly. She stared at him, and it seemed a long time passed before she could speak; actually it was no more than a few seconds. When at last the words came out they were hardly more than a gasp. "You... knew?"

He nodded, and abruptly stood and began to pace the room. "I've known since before I left."

"But—" Helpless confusion would not let her finish the sentence.

He shook his head and dragged his fingers impatiently through his hair. "I was furious at first. I was sure that you had betrayed me and I had been fool enough to fall for it, and that everything that had been between us and that I had started to believe in had just been an elaborate hoax."

Her heart clenched in horrified protest, but he went on, "And then I began to realize it wasn't you I was angry with, but myself, and not for believing in you, but for doubting you. Because"—now his tone changed; it became gentler, more reflective, and deep with the residue of remembered pain which brought a new wash of tears to her eyes—"you came into my life and turned it around, Lindsey. You gave me something to believe in when I needed it most, you reminded me of things I thought I had forgotten along with the lost idealism of my youth and—for whatever happened—it was worth that."

He crossed the room slowly, he knelt beside her and took both her hands in a firm clasp. There was pain on his face, but also courage, bitterness as well as determination. "I'm not trying to tell you it doesn't matter," he said lowly. "It matters a hell of a lot." He dropped his eyes briefly, his fingers tightened on her hand. "I guess what I'm really trying to say is that I love you, and that it's too late to change that now. It looks as though we're in this thing together, for better or worse."

She drew her hand away to gently and unsteadily stroke his bowed head, and he lifted his face to kiss her fingers, and then her lips. The passion quickly flared between them again, all the more intense now for the lack of caution and the shared struggle. She felt his arms slip beneath her and she was being carried to the bedroom; her clothing was quickly discarded in a crumpled pile on the floor, his robe joining it seconds later.

She had dreamed many times of how it would be making love with Trey. In those vivid, languorously erotic dreams they had lain in one another's arms and coaxed every nuance of sensual pleasure from each other, they had explored and lingered with exquisite slowness and painfully mounting desire and when at last fulfillment had come it had lasted forever.... The reality was quick and fiery and explosive, bordering on violence and aching with desperation. No control was possible. Her greedy passion escalated her into exploding fulfillment in only moments; she cried out and the room swam in a dizzy red-white wave, his arms crushed her ribs, and his mouth bruised hers in the violence of his own need. And when the room ceased its shuddering throb and her head began to clear, she was lying weakly in his arms, the only sound the pulsing of his heart and the only motion the unsteady rise and fall of his chest.

She looked up at him in some wonder, and saw in the misty darkness her own look of stunned confusion reflected on his face. All of these weeks of agony, of restrained desire and painful yearning, all the doubt and uncertainty, the wanting and the caution—all of it, over in a matter of minutes. She began to laugh, softly and helplessly, against his chest. "Oh, Trey," she murmured. "Nothing ever works out the way we planned, does it?"

In a moment, she felt his own response of silent laughter, and he bent to kiss her hair lightly. "No," he agreed. "I guess it never does." There was a rueful twist to his voice as he added, "I'm really a good lover, you know. I just thought I'd better tell you."

"Show me," she teased, curling her fingers about several hairs on his chest and tugging lightly.

He leaned back against the pillow and propped his arm beneath his head. "I'm too tired," he answered.

She snatched her arm pillow and struck him playfully; he quickly disarmed her and pushed her back on the bed with his hands on her shoulders, straddling her in the same motion. In the darkness his eyes snapped with laughter, and all signs of his professed exhaustion were gone.

And then, as quickly as it had come, the playfulness disappeared. He began to make love to her with his hands and his lips, slowly, beautifully, exploring to the last detail every secret of her body while allowing her the freedom to do the same with his. Passion built in steadily mounting increments, and its consummation, when at last it came, was so sweet it brought tears to her eyes, for this was the essence of the man she loved, and in sharing herself with him she had become part of him forever... and he of her.

She lay in the warm security of his arms, her head resting on his shoulder, her hand open against his chest. Peace enfolded her and radiated from him, and the silence was resonant with unspoken love. She wanted no more than to lie like this with him forever, but for the first time in her life she could no longer push away the reality. The significance of what they were and what they had done kept pushing at her, demanding attention, demanding solution. They could not stay like this forever. Tomorrow they would awake and he would be John Sinclair, senatorial candidate; she would be Lindsey Madison, advisor to the opposition. The next day he would return to devote all of his resources to winning an election; she would return to make certain he did not.

A change in the quality of the silence, or perhaps a breath or even a small movement, told her Trey was thinking the same thing. It was not something they could ignore. As hard as they tried, it would not go away, it would hang between them for the next five months and there was nothing that could change that.

And what about after the election? If he lost, she would go to Washington to fulfill her destiny in the world of politics whose call was too strong to be ignored. If he won... if he won, it meant a double loss for her, and there was no end to it, none at all.

She could not prevent a small sigh from escaping her parted lips; she tightened her hand against his chest instinctively. *If I could choose,* she thought bleakly, *from all the people in the world, one man who touched me, whose wit and charm and quick intelligence were the perfect answer to my ideal, whose dreams and hopes and aspirations were the perfect match for mine, one man whose joy could move me to ecstasy and whose pain became my own— one man to love, forever and all time—it would be only Trey.... And if I could choose from all the things I wanted for myself in the world, one calling, one ambition, one destiny that could not go unfulfilled—it would be Washington.*

How could she choose?

"Oh, Trey," she whispered brokenly, tightening her fist against his chest in a desperate attempt to fight back despair. "What are we going to do?"

He tightened his arm about her shoulders; he dropped a slow, light kiss onto her hair. "The best we can, honey," he answered softly. And as he leaned back against the pillow, she thought she heard a soft breath escape him, and he repeated, in a whisper and almost to himself, "The best we can."

Chapter Nine

The next afternoon Trey took her to a lake within walking distance of the house, where they found several aluminum row boats anchored to the bank. They selected one and climbed aboard, Trey rowing, Lindsey trailing her hand lazily in the warm water.

Trey had packed only shorts and halters for her—"It gets hot down here," he had explained innocently—and the sun bathed the exposed parts of her body with a tingling blush. He was wearing tennis shorts and an open short-sleeved shirt, and the rippling muscles of his arms and torso gleamed goldenly with the exertion. Lindsey found it a new experience in sensuality just to watch him.

Trey interrupted her languorous—and not always innocent—daydreams by inquiring, "Tell me the truth. How did you come to choose Cantrell over myself as the best man for the job?" Though the tone was light, she sensed a very real seriousness behind the question as he went on, "Was it just because he's a relative, or because he can get you the position you want in Washington?"

She answered his question honestly. "I really believe that Uncle Addison has done a good job in Washington, for both the nation and the state, and he can continue to do even more. That's the first reason. The second is," she told him without flinching, "I do want that job in Washington. More than anything."

He looked at her very steadily, letting the oars trail. "So do I," he said quietly.

For just a moment the bright sun seemed to go behind a cloud, shadowing the blissful happiness she had felt all morning. And then he picked up the oars again, as though by physical activity he would close the distance which was threatening to creep between them.

He went on casually, "It's not really going to be a hot battle for the issues, you know. It's eventually going to come down to a matter of personalities, and I don't see any reason why I can't do as good a job as Cantrell in the Senate. I'm informed, diplomatic but not too far from forceful. . . ." He glanced at her, and the lightness in his tone matched the sudden twinkle in his eye. "Charming, bright, witty—"

"Good in bed," she supplied, eyes dancing.

"Have I got your vote?" he demanded.

"Not for the Senate," she responded demurely.

He sighed. "Fickle woman."

He guided the boat to a small island on the far side of the lake and tied it off, then extended his hand to help her out. The grassy bank was dappled with sun and shadow, and sweet with the resin of pine and the scent of blooming wild flowers. She looked around her at their little grassy paradise surrounded by endless glistening blue water, and she sighed, "Oh, this is beautiful. We should have brought a picnic and spent the rest of the day here."

He kicked off his shoes and discarded his shirt. "Hungry again?"

He unsnapped his shorts and she stared at him, all thoughts of food—or the lack of it—fleeing from her mind. "What are you doing?" she demanded incredulously.

"Going swimming." He reached forward, and with a single tug, he untied the bow at her neck which fastened her halter. "And so are you!"

She caught the two falling pieces of her halter at her breasts. "I am not!"

"Shy?" he grinned, and stepping out of his shorts, he stood before her for a moment, completely nude.

"N-no." She found it very difficult to keep her eyes off the perfect lines of his unclothed body, and to maintain her line of thought. "I am not going to take off my clothes here where anyone could see! You're crazy! What if someone should come up?"

He laughed, moving his hands to her waist and unfastening the button there. "We're on an island."

She stepped away from him, removing his hands while she struggled to hold the top of her halter together. "But who knows who can see from the shore? This place is not exactly deserted, you know—stop it," she insisted, as his fingers found the zipper of her shorts. She shook her head determinedly, backing away another step. "No way."

He laughed and turned and dived into the water.

She had refastened her clothing securely by the time he surfaced and swam toward her, shaking the water from his face and calling, "Coward! It feels great. Come on!"

She smiled and stepped to the edge of the bank, bending to trail her hand in the water. His hand clasped about hers. "Come on," he urged.

She shook her head and tried to draw back, but with a sudden swift tug on her hand, he overbalanced her; she landed with a cry and a splash in the warm, clear lake. She surfaced, flailing and sputtering outraged accusations, but he covered them with his mouth. In another moment she had forgotten what she was going to say.

On the bank, he removed her wet clothes slowly and deliberately, placing warm kisses on each area of her body he uncovered. His tongue was a delicate caress on her taut nipples, the soft flesh of her abdomen, her bended knee and the sensitive inner flesh of her thigh, sending unbearable quivers of anticipation through her and once again blotting out everything but the need for him. They made love slowly in the dappled gold sunshine, and for the space of that time all else receded to the background as they clung to a love which was the only sure thing in an uncertain world.

The sun was a warm blanket of languor as she lay wrapped in his arms, and she struggled against the temptation to fall asleep right there on the grassy bed and in the security of his embrace. But after a time she stirred against him, murmuring drowsily, "What did you do with my clothes?"

"I hid them," he replied, his eyes closed.

"I'm getting sunburned," she informed him lethargically, and after a time he got up, pulling on his shorts and passing his shirt to her. He smiled at her and reached for a cigarette from the pocket of his shirt as she buttoned it over her nudity, letting his fingers linger for a moment against her breast. Then he lit the cigarette and lay back against the grass, one arm propped under his head, smoking silently.

She stretched out on her side and watched him, and for a time a contented peace lay between them. Then she could sense his thoughts drift off into moodiness, and it hurt her to know that he was being dragged into an examination of the future she had been consciously trying to avoid all day. She reached out her hand to trail lightly over his bare chest, and she said softly, "I love you."

He looked at her, and in just a moment the familiar relaxed twinkle appeared in his eye. "Yeah, sure," he retorted dryly. "But who are you going to vote for?"

She struck out at him in mock outrage, he retaliated quickly, tickling her ruthlessly, and they rolled over and over on the sunny, grassy bank in childish play.

THEY ARRIVED at her apartment at twilight the next evening. The trip back had been mostly silent, each of them searching for a way to make this good-bye less painful and to offer some encouragement for the future. And as Trey turned off the ignition and turned to her even the opportunity for a proper good-bye was lost, for his eyes flickered over her shoulder and he said softly, "Oh-oh."

She twisted to follow the direction of his gaze and to her despair saw her brother just turning away from her door. Trey's smile was rueful as he said, "I guess I'd better not come in." And he got out of the car.

Lindsey tried to push back her alarm as Trey helped her out of the car, passing her overnight bag to her, and Art slowly approached them. She did not want to look at her brother's face. And then she heard his voice, cautious, very reserved, say, "Trey."

Trey turned to him with a smile. "Arthur. It's been a while."

"Yes." Art's eyes flickered from Lindsey to Trey, and then back again, and he addressed his sister. "I've been trying to reach you all weekend."

Lindsey fumbled in her purse for her keys. "Yes, well..." She forced brightness into her tone. This was not at all the way she had wanted to end the weekend;

she would have done anything to avoid the confrontation with Art. "Now you've found me."

"I'd like to talk to you." Art's expression was completely unreadable.

"Sure," replied Lindsey cheerfully, and she turned uncertainly to Trey. So many things she wanted to say to him, and this could not have happened at a worse time.

He saved the moment by smiling at her, and bending to kiss her cheek lightly. "Hang in there, honey," he said softly. "I'll call you as soon as I can."

She swallowed hard and nodded and watched him bleakly as he called good night to Art and returned to his car.

She let herself into her apartment quickly and nervously, aware of Art's presence behind her as she hurried about the room, turning on lights and checking the thermostat, fluffing pillows and drawing the draperies and, when at last she could no longer delay, turning to face him with dread behind the defiance in her eyes.

What she saw in her brother's face was completely unexpected, as were his words. "By God," he said softly, and the light of admiration in his eyes totally caught her off guard. "You're one sharp girl, baby sister. I never would have thought it." He laughed, shortly and delightedly. "You told us to leave Sinclair to you, didn't you? By *God*!"

She caught her breath, hardly daring to believe what she thought he was suggesting. "What," she ventured cautiously, searching his face, "what do you mean?"

His eyes sparked with pleasure. "You've grown up without telling me," he replied, coming toward her with hands extended. "The only thing that bothers me is why I didn't think of it! Wars have been won by a woman since the beginning of time, why not a political campaign?'' He squeezed her hands happily. ''So tell me, what's the strategy? Have you gotten anything we can use yet?''

''Arthur, wait just a minute—''

But he went on, completely oblivious. ''You'll have to be careful, though, Sinclair's no fool. Take the goods and run, as the saying goes—''

''Stop it!'' She snatched her hands away, outrage and horror flushing her cheeks and burning in her eyes. ''You just stop it right there!'' At the confusion on her brother's face, she turned away quickly, trying to regain control of herself. In a moment she managed, somewhat more calmly, ''Trey and I—we didn't know we were on opposite sides when we met. I didn't even know who he was until it was too late. And now''—her voice softened, and she forced firmness back into it— ''it's not what you're suggesting at all; the campaign has nothing to do with what is going on between us....''

He interrupted incredulously, ''You don't mean to tell me you're in love with the ba—''

''Stop it!'' She whirled fiercely, fire in her eyes and furious warning in her tone. ''Don't say another word.''

For a moment he seemed too stunned to go further. In the flickering emotions on her brother's face she could see him incredulously reviewing the facts, assessing the situation, re-examining his position. At last he said, very lowly, ''You've done some stupid things in your life, Lindsey...''

Her lips compressed on a furious stream of expletives, her eyes flashed another warning. Art did not miss it, and he retreated slightly. ''All right,'' he said with a calmness to his tone which sounded more sinister than comforting. ''All right, so you didn't plan it.

You've never planned anything in your life, why should that surprise me? But you're here now, closer to Sinclair than anyone else, and it's not too late for you to smarten up. This is the break we've been looking for, Lindsey, and we can *win* this election if you'll only—"

"Only what?" she spat at him. Fury and revulsion pulsed within her, and she could not believe what she was hearing her brother say. "Let me tell you something, Art, this race is going to be decided by the voters of this state and no one else—not you, not me, not all your dirty tricks and sneaky schemes. I will *not* use my relationship with Trey to further our cause! How *dare* you even suggest—"

"You little fool!" His eyes swiftly went dark, his voice was a furious hiss. "Didn't it ever occur to you that *he* might be using *you*?"

She fell back, shocked and horrified. "How can you even think—I thought you knew him! He would never do such a thing...."

"God, you little idiot." His voice was heavy with incredulity. "Don't you know he would do it as quickly as I would? There *are* no rules to this game, Lindsey, haven't you learned that yet? When in hell are you going to grow up?"

She couldn't take any more. She could not stand there and listen to him say those things, trying desperately to tell herself that it wasn't her brother speaking, only his ambition.... "Get out, Art," she said stiffly. "Go away and leave me alone."

Rage smoldered in his eyes. "Lindsey," he said, very lowly, "you are a damn fool. And if we lose this election because you can't stay out of Trey Sinclair's bed—"

She slapped him. For a long time the sting of her

palm against his face seemed to echo, and she drew back in horror, a queasy feeling of revulsion rolling through her. She had not hit her brother since she was ten years old, and she was aghast at the fact that he could make her angry enough to do so now.

Slowly, he brought his fingers up to the red mark on his cheek. "All right," he admitted quietly. "I deserved that. But Addison Cantrell does not deserve what you're doing to him." He started for the door and then turned back to her as he opened it, his eyes very dark. "You think about that," he advised.

When he was gone, she rushed to the door and slammed it hard, but it was small expiation for the impotent fury that was churning inside her.

THE NEXT TWO MONTHS were spent in hard, on-the-road campaigning for all the candidates. Lindsey ached for the separation from Trey and hoped that the separation from Art would serve to heal wounds, and when he and Addison returned two weeks before the primary she was anxious to make amends. Apparently he felt the same way, for he invited her to dinner, and she eagerly accepted. It was only later she learned that his efforts had not been entirely directed toward mending broken fences.

Art "accidentally ran into" a friend of his at the dinner club and asked him to join them. His name was Greg Mann and he was nice looking, well spoken, and blond. Art guided the two of them into what he apparently felt was a well-established conversation before spotting another friend and leaving them alone. For a time Lindsey tried to continue the polite, ultimately meaningless conversation that she disliked so much, and it gradually dawned on her what Art was trying to do. She did not know whether to be angry or amused.

Greg asked her to dance, and she accepted reluctantly, not wanting to be rude. On the floor, he smiled down at her and said, "I feel as though I should apologize."

She tilted her head upward and inquired lightly, "For what?"

"Your brother's rather obvious matchmaking efforts."

She blushed and lowered her eyes. "It's nothing personal, really," she explained quickly. "It's just that I'm really not... interested, right now...."

"I know," he answered smoothly. "Art mentioned to me that you were involved with Trey Sinclair. I think that's why he was hoping I would be, shall we say, a distraction, tonight."

She laughed a little, not knowing what to say. Now she felt as though she should apologize, but he saved her the trouble. He smiled down at her again—he did have a very nice smile—and said, "I'm sorry it didn't work out, but I do understand. Trey and I are old friends," he confessed, "and all I can say is that he is one very lucky man." Again she blushed at the compliment and the look of admiration in his eyes, and then he confided to her, bending close, "Don't tell Art, but I'm voting for Sinclair."

She laughed, and the evening did not turn out to be nearly as miserable as she had expected. She decided not to reprimand Art for his efforts, for their relationship was still too tenuous to bear much strain, and she was certain he meant well.

TREY DID NOT ARRIVE BACK in the city until three days before the primary. He called her, but the brief conversation throbbed with the poignancy of things unsaid and the frustration of all that separated them. And the following days would be too frantic for them to spare even a moment for one another.

On the night of the election Lindsey had been at campaign headquarters for almost twenty-four hours straight, living on coffee and hamburgers and snatched naps in the private office. Adrenaline surged, and excitement pulsed in the air as the first election results came in, and Lindsey anxiously followed two candidates: Addison Cantrell, leading easily in the first reporting districts, and John Sinclair, making a strong showing in the preliminary tallies. By midnight, the final word was in — Addison Cantrell by a landslide. The place went wild. Lindsey, accepting hugs and slaps on the back, tried to share in the enthusiasm, but something knotted tensely within her until she heard the news she had really been waiting for: The person Addison would be running against in the final election for the Senate seat was John Sinclair.

For the next two hours Addison made speeches of thanks and encouragement, people laughed and drank and congratulated themselves and made enthusiastic plans for the final phase of the battle, and Lindsey was removed by some distance from it, her emotions in a turmoil.

She really did not know how she felt. This was what she had waited for, counted on, the moment she had unconsciously been sure would solve all their problems. Well, it hadn't. She was happy, of course, for Addison and herself; they had all worked so hard and this was the fruit of their labor, the first hurdle cleared. And she was happy for Trey. It was what he wanted, and how could she not be happy for him? She *was* happy, and proud of him, but, oh, it would have been so much more uncomplicated if only he had lost....

And then, close to two o'clock, the atmosphere in

the room changed. It did not become exactly hushed, but curious; there was a thin ripple of excitement, a variation in the quality of the babbling voices which surrounded her. Lindsey turned from the conversation in which she was absently engaged and saw Trey Sinclair walk into the room.

She watched in stunned amazement, her heart leaping to her throat in the pure joy of seeing him again, as he shook hands with Uncle Addison and the two men exchanged pleasantries which she could not hear. He made the same gesture to her brother, who received him only slightly less civilly, and slowly he made his way across the crowded room toward her, pausing to speak to those he knew, an easy, relaxed smile on his face. And then he was standing beside her and she was looking up into those dark eyes, sparkling with pleasure and the deep light of tender passion she had come to know so well, and he was saying beneath the gaiety of the crowd all about them, "I believe the term is 'shake hands and come out fighting.' It seemed only civil."

She had never loved him more, and her face shone with it. The reflection of her own joy was in his eyes, and the air between them practically quivered with it. He said softly, "Is there a back door to this place?"

She nodded wordlessly and led the way.

THEY MADE LOVE with a ferocity and desperation that rivaled the first time. It had been weeks since she had seen him and in only a matter of hours he must leave her again.... She did not know how she could let him go. She clung to him, trembling with the aftermath of passion and the knowledge that too soon she must let him go again, and she whispered, "Oh, Trey, how can we go on like this? It isn't fair!"

He stroked her hair gently and said nothing. What

was there to be said? But gradually she began to sense that his silence was due to more than just mourning their situation. There was a moodiness about him, and a tension in his muscles which was not usually there after love. It was something that seemed to have been building up throughout their weeks of separation without her being aware of it, and it frightened her. When she could stand the silence no longer, she ventured softly, her head still resting against his chest, "I didn't congratulate you. I'm glad you won."

He reached over her to take a cigarette from his shirt pocket, and his tone was curt. "Are you? I should say 'surprised' would be more accurate."

She moved onto her pillow, bunching it under her cheek as she positioned herself to look at him. In the brief flare of the cigarette lighter his face was grim, the posture of his body taut. She said quietly, trying not to be hurt, "That's not fair, Trey."

"Damn it, Lindsey how am I supposed to feel?" The tip of the cigarette glowed, he exhaled the fragrant smoke shortly. "Am I supposed to just ignore the fact that the woman I love doesn't even have enough confidence to support my campaign? How am I supposed to convince the thousands of citizens of this state that I'm the best man for the job when I can't even convince you? You talk about not fair—what you're doing to me is not fair!"

She turned miserably on her back, staring at the ceiling, dragging her fingers through her hair and trying not to cry. "You know that isn't it," she said. There was weariness in her voice, moisture on her lashes. "We disagree on some of the issues, but we can't help that. I have to live with my conscience, Trey, and even though right now it's not easy, I've sworn loyalty to Addison Cantrell. I couldn't live with myself, and I could never ask for your respect, if I went back on that vow. You do understand, don't you?" she pleaded.

There was a long silence. At last he said, very quietly, "I understand." He sighed. "I'm sorry, Lindsey. I guess the stress is getting to me. And I can't help thinking how much more tonight would mean if I only knew you had voted for me."

She started to reach for him, and then an unfathomable thought struck her. She sat bolt upright in bed, her hands flew to her face, and she gasped, "Oh, my God!" Horror was in her eyes, her voice was high and choked. "I forgot to vote!"

He looked at her for a moment, her stunned incredulity reflected in his face. And then he burst into laughter. He laughed and laughed, and he drew her into his arms and she laughed too, helplessly and hopelessly, until they were both too weak to do anything else.

DURING THE NEXT THREE MONTHS the campaigning began in earnest, hot and heavy and relentless on both sides. Lindsey's only contact with Trey was a few minutes each day on the phone or a few hours snatched here and there at her apartment, usually between the hours of midnight and dawn when they were both too exhausted to do anything other than hold one another and talk in lethargic, perfunctory tones about things that didn't matter. With each good-bye the agony grew worse. This is definitely, thought Lindsey wearily, no way to conduct a love affair.

"It's almost over," he told her one evening as he once again said good-bye. He was leaving the next morning for a three-week tour of the southern part of the state. "Just hold on to that thought. It won't be much longer now."

Yes, it was almost over, but for better or for worse? She could not face thoughts of the future when it took every ounce of her energy just to get through another day.

The summer leaves turned to gold and then to brown, a chill breeze blew down from the North to frost the morning grass, and the tension at campaign headquarters steadily increased. Addison Cantrell was still strong in the polls, but John Sinclair was rising fast. Everyone was worried, and Lindsey was no exception. Only now she was no longer certain what she was most worried about: Uncle Addison's winning or losing.

The last month of the campaign would be concentrated around the heavily populated capital, and both candidates were at home. This should have meant an opportunity for Lindsey and Trey to resume a more-or-less normal relationship, but the truth was far from it. Now, more than ever, every spare moment was accounted for, and that was why Lindsey had leaped so eagerly at the chance to be with Trey tonight.

Art, on his way out the door, asked her that morning, "Are you coming to the dinner tonight?"

She checked her calendar quickly. Sure enough, Uncle Addison was scheduled to speak at a dinner for a group of influential businessmen, and both she and Art usually accompanied him at such affairs. She had forgotten it, but that was not to be remarked. There had been so much crowding up her hours these past weeks that she had to constantly carry a list with her to remind her what to do next. "No," she answered. "I'm not really needed there."

Art gave her a peculiar look. "Other plans?"

She faced him bravely. "Yes, as a matter of fact. I'm going to a party at Trey's house." There was no reason to hide it. Trey had assured her it was nothing political, just a gathering of a few close friends and a chance for him to relax and catch his breath, and he had wanted her there. She wouldn't have refused if she had had a dozen dinners to attend.

Art's dry little smile was almost ugly. "Still working both sides of the street, Lindsey?"

She turned back to her desk, stiffening against the sight of him and the tone of his voice, and she did not see when he left.

She had planned to get away by six, to allow herself plenty of time to shower and change, for she did not want to miss one moment of Trey's company. But just as she was slipping into her jacket and picking up her purse, a familiar figure walked into the office. Greg Mann greeted her pleasantly as he approached.

"I was looking for your brother," he said. "It's a nice bonus to see you again, too. How've you been?"

She returned his smile. He really was a nice person, and it was a shame they had met under such unfavorable circumstances. Even though she was in a rush, she could spare a few minutes to talk to him.

"You wouldn't ask that if you'd ever worked a political campaign," she replied with a laugh. "It's nice to see you again, too, but I'm afraid you've missed Art. I don't expect him back today."

"Oh." He looked disappointed. "That's too bad."

She offered, "Is there anything I can help you with?"

"Not with Art, no," he answered. "But"—he glanced at her hesitantly—"there might be something else you could do for me, if you don't mind."

"Anything I can," she agreed pleasantly.

He propped his briefcase on her desk and took out a manila envelope. "Would you by chance be seeing Trey any time soon?"

"Tonight, as a matter of fact," she answered.

Relief crossed his face. "Good. His firm has been doing some work for me, and they've needed these papers for weeks now. I just finished them today, and I have to catch a plane in an hour. If you could just see that Trey gets them, I would sure feel a lot better."

She took the envelope from him and agreed, "Sure. I'd be glad to."

His smile was radiant, instantly charming. "Thanks a lot, Lindsey. Give Trey my best, and—good luck to both of you, I guess."

She laughed, and he gave her a gay wave as he left.

As she was leaving, the phone rang, and she had to stop to answer it, leaving the envelope on her desk. She was halfway out the door before she remembered it, and as she went back to get it she discovered she had also left her purse. She sighed in weary exasperation with herself. It was only getting worse.

BY THE TIME SHE ARRIVED at Trey's house several other cars were already there, she could dimly hear the music from behind the brightly lit windows. She hurried through the chill air, her heart already beginning to soar with the anticipation of seeing him again. She was at the door when she remembered the yellow envelope lying on the front seat of her car; with a small hiss of impatience, she ran back to get it.

There were no more than a dozen couples inside, the talk was intimate and laughter was light. Firelight flickered on the dark paneling and glasses clinked against the background of the music. Lindsey scanned the room for Trey and did not see him immediately; she decided he was probably in the kitchen. The first thing she did, after slipping out of her jacket, was to place the envelope securely on the mantel, where she could be certain it would not be lost. Then she went to look for Trey.

They met as he was coming out of the kitchen. His eyes lit up as he saw her; he made his way slowly toward her through the other couples to clasp her hands, his bright eyes avidly scanning her face, her bare shoulders, her clinging, gauzy white evening gown. His eyes told her she had never looked more beautiful, and she felt every inch of it.

"I can see your freckles," he teased softly, one hand leaving hers momentarily to brush lightly across the bare part of her chest.

"As long as no one notices but you," she returned, "I don't mind."

Both his hands squeezed hers, he bent to kiss her lips very lightly, very briefly. Reluctance and yearning were in his eyes as he straightened up. "I hope it doesn't bother you," he said, "all the people. You don't know any of them and there's no reason they should know you, so it shouldn't be embarrassing. This party was rather obligatory, and I couldn't pass up the chance to be with you—even in these circumstances."

She smiled and assured him, "I don't mind." To be with him, under any circumstances, was all she wanted.

"Good," he said softly, and the light of passion began to kindle in his eyes as they traveled over her face, to the deep neckline of her dress, to rest at last longingly on her lips. "Because I think I do. Do you think all these good people would notice if you and I were to disappear for an hour or two?"

"Definitely," she told him, her lips tightening with a demure little smile. "You're only three weeks away from the election, Sinclair. Don't blow it now."

He laughed and drew her into his arms, and for the next hour they danced, bodies close, arms about each other, his cheek against her hair, and, as always, everything else was forgotten when she was in his arms.

It was much later that she remembered she had been entrusted with a mission. "Oh," she murmured, looking up at him. "I almost forgot—I brought something for you."

"I know," he smiled. "You."

She snuggled against his shoulder, utterly content, and then she answered, "No. A package. Legal papers, from Greg Mann."

He looked down at her. "Who?"

"Greg Mann," she repeated glancing up at him. "He said your firm was doing some work for him."

He looked puzzled. "I don't know anyone by that name."

She stopped dancing. "Why, that's strange. He said he was a good friend of yours."

He lifted an eyebrow with a slight shrug. "Since this campaign started, seems as though everyone in the state is a good friend of mine. Where are the papers?"

She turned to show him, and then, as if on cue, the front door burst open. Lindsey turned, and she watched in incredulous shock the scene from a comic horror as a dark-uniformed figure appeared on the threshold, then two, then three, and then the room was swarming with police officers, all of them with guns drawn, grim faces, and cautious eyes.

And a voice carried over the din of disturbance, "Everyone maintain your positions. This is a raid."

Chapter Ten

Lindsey's first instinct was to burst into laughter. She glanced at Trey and saw incredulity was reflected in his face, but whatever hint of amusement might have been there was quickly wiped away as one of the officers walked up to him and handed him a warrant. Trey's eyes grew dark as he scanned it, his lips whitened and compressed into a thin line.

Lindsey, touching his arm, whispered, "What is it?" but he appeared not to have heard her. And from that moment on everything was such a flurry that she could do more than watch, amazed and speechless and paralyzed with alarm. It seemed to take forever, but it was amazingly quick. The officers began to disperse over the house, opening drawers and closets and pulling out books and displacing sofa cushions; the outraged, confused protests of the other guests were a dim, discordant babble, and Trey only stood there, letting them violate his property and his privacy, saying nothing, not moving.

Lindsey wanted to shake him, she wanted to cry out to snap him back into awareness and register her protest at this desecration of his rights, but in the next moment the officer in charge was called over to the fireplace, where another officer had found the envelope she had put on the mantel. They opened it.

"Why, that's—" began Lindsey in a loud, outraged voice, and Trey's hand clamped down hard on hers. His face was like stone.

The officer came over to them, a small clear bag of some white powder extended in his open hand. He said, "Mr. Sinclair, this was found in an envelope with your name on it."

Trey said nothing.

Lindsey's frantic gaze flew from Trey to the officer to the as yet unidentified symbol of accusation in his hand, and she whispered, "What is it? Why are you—"

"Cocaine," answered the officer briefly, and looked again at Trey.

The shock was brief and devastating and dizzying, but it lasted no longer than the time it took to galvanize her into action. "But that's impossible!" she cried. "That's not—"

Trey warned sharply, "Lindsey!"

But she ignored him, insisting desperately, "It's not his! You can't accuse him of—I'm the one who—"

Trey's fingers dug painfully into her arm and he said lowly, "Lindsey, as your attorney I advise you strongly not to say another word."

But she did. She said a great many other words, and she saw the expression on Trey's face go from anger to frustration to weary resignation as he retreated from her by inches.

The scene at the police station was a blur of terror and confusion. She repeated her story so many times it became something like a desperate recording. She told them how Greg Mann had come by headquarters and asked her to deliver the envelope, and no, she hadn't known what was in it, couldn't they tell it had not been opened? In despair she racked her brain trying to remember more about Greg Mann, and she realized in horror she had known *nothing* about him; she had become friends with a total stranger...and even Art's introduction had not made it any safer.

She and Trey were interrogated separately, and though she begged for information about Trey, she got nothing. Surely he could not be accused of a crime of which he had no knowledge; it did not occur to her that the same thing could happen to her.

Art came down, and he, too, was questioned privately, presumably about the character and whereabouts of Greg Mann. After a time an officer came in to the bare, stark room in which she had been asked to wait and told her she was free to go. Outside, she saw one of Trey's aides, Bob Cagle, and she went to him quickly.

"What's going to happen to Trey?" she demanded desperately. "Surely they can't hold him.... Isn't it obvious he didn't know anything about this?"

Bob's eyes were very cold. "It's obvious," he replied, "that he was framed."

"But who—" And then she drew back in horror. Who, indeed? Only someone who wanted to make certain Trey was not the next U.S. senator, someone who— Her hand went to her throat, her eyes were dark with shock. "I swear to you," she whispered, "I didn't know! I would never—"

"You'll understand, Miss Madison," replied Bob coldly, "if I say I don't quite believe you." And he turned away.

Art came out, his face grim and his posture tense. Without a word, he took her arm and hurried her outside into his waiting car.

During the trip home shock whirled and reverberated through her so fiercely it precluded speech. She had never been in a police station before and the sights and sounds clung to her like a bad odor. Over and over

224 A Matter of Trust

she chastised herself, *If only I hadn't been so trusting, so eager to please a perfect stranger, if only I had been just a little suspicious of someone who asked me to deliver a package he could have just as easily delivered himself....* She remembered the many times she had almost forgotten the envelope, left it behind, had to come back to retrieve it. If only.... If only she had given it to Trey as soon as she had arrived, instead of forgetting about it. He would have opened it and he would have seen what was happening.... But no, with her typical vagueness, she had placed it in clear sight and never thought to mention it to Trey... until it was too late.

Horror battered her in pulsing waves. What would Trey think? Would he, with his aide, believe she had done it on purpose, that as a last-minute resort in a desperate campaign, she had coldly calculated the one way to insure a victory for her team? Would he believe in her innocence?

Whatever happened, his political aspirations were ruined. The press had been looking for something just like this, and so, she realized dully, had the Addison Cantrell re-election committee. If Trey were arrested, his career could be ruined as well, and if he were convicted he would be disbarred.... All because of her.

Art took her to Addison's house, and she did not even feel surprise as he guided her up the steps of her uncle's stately colonial residence. He explained, "I called Addison from the police station. We both thought it would be best if you weren't alone tonight."

She nodded dully as the door was opened by her uncle, obviously much distraught and in his dressing gown and slippers, and she allowed herself to be bundled into the warm, book-lined study, and when she next noticed her surroundings she was sitting on the sofa with a glass of brandy in her hand.

The two men, after seeing to her comfort and physical well-being, retreated to the other side of the room and left her in silence. She forced herself to drink the brandy because she knew it would give her a semblance of the strength she needed so desperately right now; she breathed deeply and tried to clear her head for an unvarnished perspective on the situation. She needed to think. Trey needed her and there must be something she could do; for once in her life she must take control of the situation, for this was no time to break down.

Firmly, and in surges, her courage began to return, and with it, the clear, efficient, decisive mode of thinking, which had characterized her professional life but had never intruded before into her private one. First, she had to know the facts, and the haunted look disappeared from her eyes as she demanded of Art, "What about Mann? Have they picked him up yet?"

He shook his head, his eyes upon the yellowish liquid he was swirling in his glass. "I imagine he's safely in Mexico by now."

"But how can that be?" she insisted angrily. "How can he just get away with this? You know him, we have his name—"

"Criminals on the run rarely use their real names, Lindsey," interjected Uncle Addison quietly.

Her eyes went from her uncle back to Art. "But you—" And then a thought so horrible it was almost unspeakable dawned on her. She tried to push it back, but it refused to be subdued, and she inquired cautiously of her brother, "What *do* you know about him, anyway? How did you meet him? Who is he?"

Art shrugged uncomfortably. "Doesn't matter."

"Yes, it *does* matter," she insisted, trying to keep her voice calm, her tone rational. "Are you in the habit of associating with drug-dealers and junkies?"

"Oh, for God's sake, Lindsey," he burst out impatiently. "He was neither! He was just an ordinary guy and I never really investigated his personal habits. I can't tell you any more than I told the police. So he got his hands on a little cocaine—anyone can do that. What's the big deal, anyway?"

"What's the big deal?" For just that moment, she lost control. "A man's career is ruined, that's all! An innocent man is looking at a felony record and possible prison time and you're asking me *what's the big deal?*"

Art took a quick, impatient gulp of his drink. "Don't be a baby, Lindsey. Do you really think Trey Sinclair is going to let anything like that happen to him? He's got more connections in this city than I have, and he'll be home drinking coffee out of his own pot before dawn." He turned to her, the lines of his face forcefully smoothing out, an assumed gentleness in his tone. "Look, no one's talking about a man's career. Even if the district attorney weren't Trey's best friend and biggest supporter, he would be a fool to try to press charges. Even the police know they don't have a case. Trey Sinclair will go home to his multimillion-dollar corporation and his cozy little law practice none the worse for wear, I promise you. The important thing— the only thing that should matter to you—is that he's out of the race. Doesn't that mean anything to you?"

She stared at him, horror swelling into a cold hard lump in the pit of her stomach. But even the revulsion she felt could not mute the rapid, efficient working of her mind, and it all became unbearably clear. She could count on the fingers of one hand the people who knew about her relationship with Trey, those who knew that of all people he might be on his guard against she was not one of them. Three weeks before the election his popularity was skyrocketing, and how many times had she heard Art say in the past few days that something had to be done quickly? Oh, it was so simple, so terrifyingly, beautifully simple. Only this morning she had told Art about Trey's party; this afternoon a man who had wormed his way into her confidence arrived with a package for her to deliver. Less than an hour after she had made the delivery the police showed up, knowing exactly what they were looking for. It was so transparent it was almost absurd. And who better as courier than the innocent, absentminded, ridiculously gullible Lindsey?

She said flatly, "You set him up."

An expression flickered over Art's face which revealed the truth in a second, and nausea rolled in her stomach. He said, "Lindsey, don't be—"

She stood slowly She felt cold to the tips of her fingers and the voice which came from her throat did not seem to belong to her at all. It was distant, faraway, separated from the girl she had been only moments ago by the space of a lifetime.

"You set him up," she repeated carefully, "and you used me to do it. You used *me*. It never occurred to you that I might end up in jail—"

"Oh, Lindsey don't be stupid," he burst out impatiently, finishing his drink in one gulp. "I would never let anything like that happen to you."

Uncle Addison was watching her carefully; Art refused to look at her. This was her brother, in whom she believed, her big brother, her protector, her confidant, and her friend for twenty-nine years...the man she had loved and admired and modeled herself after, to whom she had turned in times of trouble...the man she had never known. And strangely, beyond the sick rolling grief in the pit of her stomach she could only remember one thing about him at this moment:

He was a man who didn't like to lose, no matter what the cost.

Somehow her voice supported her one more time, though her legs were growing weak and her hands were trembling violently. She said, "Well, you're not going to let this happen to Trey, either." She started toward the door, unaware of the enormous effort it took to place one foot in front of the other. "I'm going to the police station and tell them the truth right now."

She had almost made it to the door before his voice, tight and thick with venom, spat out, "Fine. You just do that. And while you're at it, you remember the only thing that's standing between you and a jail sentence is me!"

She whirled, a silent gasp on her lips, horror lodged in her throat. In her brother's eyes she saw the ultimate truth: that he would do it. He could ruin a man's life and he could have charges brought against his own sister and not feel a moment's regret, because nothing would ever stand between Art and what he wanted.

"Lindsey..." Uncle Addison started toward her gently. "For God's sake, child, think a moment. The damage has already been done; there's nothing you can do to help now. This thing is too close to backfiring on us now; if you go to the police it will all blow sky-high and the campaign will be ruined. All we've worked for—"

She stared at him, a new wave of revulsion assaulting her. "The campaign? You—you can't mean you *approve* of what Art's done! You stood right here and heard him say—"

"Lindsey." His sigh was regretful, but it came nothing near to reflecting the shock she was feeling. "Of course the entire matter is unfortunate, but these things happen in politics every day. The important thing is not to get caught..." He shot a dark look at

Art. "And I'm afraid your brother's efforts in that direction were not very conscientious."

It swept over her in cold, devastating certainty, the final truth of it. Not only had Uncle Addison approved, he had *known*; from the beginning he and Art had plotted it together. This was the man in whom she had placed her trust, the man whose honesty and integrity she had supported so determinedly, the man she had chosen even over her love....

She groped blindly for the door. She heard voices calling her back, but her need was only to run. The keys were still in Art's car and she took it without hesitation. *Grand theft auto,* she thought a little hysterically, and then she thought nothing else because the awful, racking sobs were building up in her throat, and she forced them back, coldly and decisively, concentrating on her driving.

It was only when she was safely inside her apartment that she let the full impact of it all sweep her. Shakily, she wandered about the room, trying to busy herself with the empty motions of normalcy, but the tears which flowed down her cheeks were unstaunchable and the silent sobs which racked her defied her courage. Emptiness, like none she had ever known, washed over her when at last she had given in to the devastation and sobbed her rage and her grief out loud to the empty room. She lay at last on the sofa, dry-eyed and completely spent, and her mind began to work again in the calm, coldly rational manner which had become almost second nature to her now. She got up and picked up the shattered pieces of her life, automatically making preparations for the new day which was only hours away.

At seven o'clock, she left the house, locking her door behind her.

Chapter Eleven

A cold, damp wind blew off the Atlantic, whipping through Lindsey's hair and stinging her cheeks with salt. The rolling water was dark and the sky was bleak, like Lindsey's mood.

She did not even notice that her father had come to stand beside her until he spoke. "Dreary thoughts for a dreary day, hmm?" he commented.

She smiled at him a little wanly and stuffed her hands into her pockets against the chapping cold. "I'm afraid I haven't been very good company for you," she answered.

His gaze followed the soaring flight of a gull and the wind tugged at his long gray hair. "No one asked you to be," he replied mildly.

She hunched her shoulders uncomfortably. "Anyway, I'm sorry I invaded your sanctum with my depressing little problems. I didn't mean to drag you into this."

For a moment he said nothing, but there was no need for him to say anything. He had given her all the support she had needed these past three weeks with his silence, his simple routine, his comforting presence. Instinctively he had known that she had not needed his sympathy or his advice, only time...to adjust, and grow. She was not certain whether she had done either, but the pain seemed less acute now. She was coping.

After a time he commented, "The election is tomorrow, isn't it?"

She glanced at him. He had listened to her story without remark, and it had become almost an unspoken agreement between them that it should not be referred to again. She wondered that he would bring it up now.

Before leaving Atlanta, she had gone to the newspapers with her story. In a game where all rules were off, it had seemed the most efficient way of handling a very distasteful situation. The charges had been dropped against Trey, so nothing she could tell the police would have made a difference—they certainly couldn't prove anything against Art or Addison, and only a half-hearted attempt was being made to find the elusive Greg Mann. Her final duty in a situation in which words like "loyalty" and "honor" had been cheapened to the point of worthlessness was to make certain the public had the facts. The next morning she had read with little surprise and a dry twist to her lips the headline, SINCLAIR PARTY RAIDED IN COCAINE BUST and, in much smaller print beginning on page twelve, her own story, "Cantrell Aide Charges Corruption." *Well, Trey,* she had thought dully, closing the paper, *I've done the best I can. I guess it's in your corner now.*

She had not heard from Trey. She had not answered the phone, and she had left town less than twenty-four hours later. She supposed he blamed her, and why shouldn't he? If he lost this election it would be her fault... and she did not even know whether he had decided to continue to run. If it had been herself, she supposed she would not. The results were pretty well cut-and-dried, and she did not see the point in going through the motions of a formal voting process.

Her father went on mildly, "Didn't you mention to me you were in love with a man who had a pretty big stake in that election?"

She gave a short laugh. "My loving him just about ruined his life."

"Do you think he feels that way?"

She hesitated for a long time. How could he feel any differently? Trey knew the world as she was only just beginning to see it, he knew anything was possible when power and ambition came into the play, and if nothing else he would hate her for her own stupidity which had led to her part in the fiasco. So many times he had tried to warn her to wise up.... Well, at last, she had. She said, very softly, "I don't know."

"You mean you don't know him well enough," elucidated her father.

She shrugged. "I thought I knew Addison. I thought I knew him well enough to believe in him. I guess my judgment leaves something to be desired."

Her father ran his long, sun-browned fingers through his chest-length gray beard, and he said at last, thoughtfully, "You know that if this man loves you he is only going to believe the best of you. And he won't let anything stand in the way of your happiness together."

She looked bleakly out over the churning, storm-tossed ocean. "Oh, Daddy," she sighed. "What Trey loved of me...isn't there anymore. I'm not the same girl he fell in love with, and I never will be again. It's all so complicated.... I really don't want to think about it now."

"I'm afraid you have to, daughter," replied her father soberly, and he turned back toward the house. "We've got company."

Her first reaction was a jolt of anticipation mixed peculiarly with a rush of joy as she turned and saw the expensive white car parked before her father's modest little beach cottage, for she thought it was Trey. But immediately that emotion drained into a sort of resigned numbness as a woman stepped out of the eaves, her soft fur coat hugged about her shoulders and her arm uplifted in greeting.

"Well, Dan, you old codger," Irene MacDonald greeted Lindsey's father. "I'll bet you're surprised to see me, aren't you?"

"Not particularly," replied her father. "I knew it was only a matter of time. You do have the most uncanny instinct for unearthing people whose only wish is to be left to their privacy."

Irene was not offended. She tapped his arm lightly in reprimand and retorted, "Then it will come as a blow to your eternal ego that I did not come to see you, but your daughter. Could we go inside out of the wind?"

Irene looked utterly out of place in her designer suit and sable coat amidst the clutter of tools and clay and sketches which littered the cabin, yet at the same time she looked ultimately at home. Lindsey's father silently served coffee to the two women at the kitchen table, and then left them without another glance to take up his work where he had left off.

Lindsey sipped her coffee, waiting for the other woman to speak first. Finally, she did, and it was only to say, "You've lost weight."

Lindsey forced out the question which had to be asked, uncertain whether the pain would be worse if the answer were yes or no. "Did Trey send you?"

Though her eyes were steady — *so like Trey's,* Lindsey thought with an unexpected lurch of pain — Irene answered obliquely. "One of the most important aspects to my relationship with my son is that I never interfere in his affairs. He will have to forgive me this time, because I just couldn't stand by and watch him suffer any longer."

Lindsey dropped her eyes, uncertain how to react to the torrent of emotions which were whirling within her. She asked, "What has he done about the campaign?"

"Nothing," answered Irene, sipping her coffee.

Lindsey looked at her, startled. One of her greatest dreads had been that Trey would be forced to do something equally as underhanded to retaliate against the Cantrell campaign if he had a hope of staying in the running. As much as her own experience had hurt her, the thought that Trey might have been corrupted as well hurt more.

"You mean . . . he's dropped his campaign?"

Irene shook her head. "I mean he has done nothing. He has cleared his name to his satisfaction, and now he will let the voters decide." She smiled a little. "I'm afraid sometimes these distasteful tactics have a way of backfiring, and your uncle is not looking quite as saintly as he might have once. Trey is still a strong contender, but you, my dear"—there was sympathy in her eyes—"I'm afraid your reputation has gotten the worst of it. You seem to have been labeled by the press as something of a spy."

"It doesn't matter," Lindsey said softly, and it really didn't. "As long as Trey is all right." And then a horrible thought struck her. "Irene," she said desperately, "you know that I—"

Irene waved it away briefly, sipping again from her cup. "I know."

Lindsey dropped her eyes, relieved. "Do you think Trey has a chance?" she asked in a moment.

"He has a chance," said his mother. "Which of

course is why I'm here today. I want you to come back with me."

Lindsey shook her head. "There's no point."

"Do you still love my son?" Irene asked directly.

Lindsey took a breath. "That—that's not the issue," she managed.

"And what is, may I ask?"

Lindsey floundered helplessly. How could she put it into words? It would never be the same between them. She could not ask Trey to love her, she was not the same girl he had once known. And she was not worthy to love him. Love without trust was just an empty shell, and she did not think she would ever trust anyone again.

She said, almost in a whisper, "I can't... ask him to forgive me for what I did."

Irene replied steadily, "I would say that's his choice, wouldn't you?" And then she reached forward and clasped Lindsey's hand firmly. "Lindsey, you mustn't let this thing scar you permanently. What happened was disagreeable and traumatic, it may be the worst thing that will ever happen to you... or it may not. You have to *go on*." She straightened up, her eyes determined and her words firm. "The girl I first met had the courage to work in one of the hottest political campaigns in this state, to love one candidate and support the other, and to remain loyal to both. Isn't there any of that spirit left, Lindsey? Because, believe me, if you start running from unpleasantness now, you'll be running for the rest of your life. I can't let you do that."

Lindsey smiled at her, slowly and wistfully. "I'm not running," she said. "I only wish I could. I've accepted what's happened, and I know I have to get on with my life." She stood. "I'll go back with you. I suppose I owe it to myself to see this thing through."

LINDSEY WATCHED the election returns alone in her apartment, for the first time in ten years away from the madness and the frenzied excitement of a campaign headquarters on election night. Irene had asked Lindsey to stay with her, but she had wanted to be by herself... and there was something entirely too symbolic about watching the election returns with Trey's mother.

Two hours after the polls closed Addison Cantrell was predicted the clear winner. But Lindsey was too much of a professional to accept anything as certain until the last vote was counted. Anxiously she watched as, by midnight, Trey Sinclair began to make a strong showing, and two hours later the results began to astound even the newscasters. Sinclair was moving up fast, especially in the outlying districts in which he had campaigned so heavily. This surprised no one more than Lindsey, for it had been almost certain that the recent scandal would cost him those rural votes. The only question was, would the loyalty of those voters be enough to win the election?

She sat through the night, tensely, anxiously watching the impossible happen before her very eyes. By three o'clock, the results were close enough to require a recount—in Trey's favor.

Suddenly she wanted to call him. More than anything, she wanted to just call him and tell him she was on his side, she believed in him, she was pulling for him. She even got up and went to the telephone, tears of pride and happiness flooding her vision. No matter what the recount showed, Trey was the clear winner in her eyes. He had come closer than even the experts had imagined and he had taken the lead—and he had done it all honestly.

But then she let her hand drop from the telephone;

she slowly walked away. All those words of congratula-
tion and support were really coming just a bit too late;
she did not think he would want to hear them from her.

The final results were not announced until nine
o'clock in the morning: It was Trey Sinclair, by a clear
margin.

Exhaustion and tension muted her first burst of enthusiastic joy. He had won. It was what he wanted, what
she wanted—yet the victory seemed empty without
someone to share it with.

Keyed up and restless, assaulted by too many complicated emotions to analyze, she could not stay con-
fined to her apartment. She got into her car and began
driving, and soon she found herself parking her car at
Sweetwater Creek.

The day was misty, cold and overcast, and the park
was deserted. It was so much like the first day she had
come there that she could almost feel Trey's presence
beside her, walking the same trail, thinking the same
silent thoughts. He had found forgiveness for her on
that day, she realized slowly, and faith in her against all
odds. She had come here today to try to find some way
to forgive herself.

Long since she made peace within herself about Art
and Addison. Bitterness was self-destructive, and hat-
ing them or blaming them was pointless. They were no
different than a thousand other men faced with big
fights and bad odds in a world where integrity was fast
becoming an endangered species. It did not make what
they had done right, nor in any way excuse them or
anyone like them, but Lindsey had found an accep-
tance for it. She had faced the worst and, she realized
as she slowly walked the deserted path she had once
taken with Trey by her side, she had emerged the
stronger for it.

The water was icy as she climbed once again onto her boulder; it soaked the cuffs of her jeans and sprayed on her face, but she hardly noticed the cold. Soon she was lost in the rushing and thundering of the water, taking strength from it as she finally found her peace.

How differently she had imagined this day to be only a month ago. She had dreaded the final outcome almost as much as she looked forward to it, for then she had been torn between two loyalties. The choice between her life's ambition and her only love no longer hung over her, for she had lost both of them.

The only thing she cared about now was that Trey did not hate her. He was going to Washington and she was desperately glad, but she did not think she could bear it if she knew he was leaving with bitterness in his heart to replace the love and trust which had once been there. If only she could see him, one more time....

And then, as she stood to make her way back to the shore, she did. He was standing on the bank, watching her, and it was so much like the last time that for a moment she was certain the figure was only a ghost of her imagination. Her heart leaped to her throat and began to pound there, and as she made her way across the stepping-stones she slipped and almost fell. He reached out his hand in an automatic protective gesture and then she knew it was for real. The shock and the joy and then the anxiety which flooded her was almost paralyzing.

She stood before him on solid ground looking up at him with wonder and question in her eyes, and she was surprised she could speak. "How... did you know I was here?" she managed.

His smile was a little wan. "I didn't," he admitted. "I just needed to be here, and" — his voice fell fractionally — "I guess we still think alike."

She looked at him, trying to keep the anxiety and the pleading out of her eyes, wanting only to touch him, to hold him, to tell him that she loved him... and that she did not expect him to still love her, if only he would forgive her. But something restrained her.

Lightly, he brought his hand up to touch her tangled and water-frizzed hair; his small smile did not reach his eyes. He said, "You look awful."

"So do you," she whispered, thinking he had never looked more wonderful. The lost sleep was evident in eyes that were bloodshot and puffy, and he looked pale. He was freshly shaven and well-groomed for the cameras, but the lines about his lips were grim; his face looked haggard. He, too, had lost weight.

He dropped his hand, and then his eyes. He said, very quietly, "I was coming for you today."

Hope leaped, a hope that was too wonderful to be believed, and with her newly discovered caution, she would not let herself believe it entirely. She had to ask the question she dreaded, not allowing herself to expect the answer she needed so desperately. She clasped her hands tightly before her and stilled the quivering of her lips, her eyes fixed upon his unrevealing face anxiously.

"Trey..." She forced the words out. "Do you—can you...do you forgive me?"

His eyes flew to hers, and amazement mixed with incredulity was there. "Forgive you?" he repeated blankly. "Lindsey, did you ever really think...You didn't believe I blamed you!" A frustrated sigh escaped him, he ran his fingers through his hair in a gesture of impotence and anger, half turning from her. "My God, Lindsey, I thought you trusted me more than that! I thought you knew me!" When he turned to her again the frustration was still in his eyes, but it was directed at himself, and not her, and softened with a reflected pain. "Lindsey, don't tell me you've been torturing yourself all this time with that. The whole thing was so transparent a fool could see through it, and how could you think I would ever doubt you? Lindsey"—his voice softened, his face pleaded for her belief—"I told you once I don't make commitments lightly. I committed myself to you one spring day right on this spot, and I meant it forever."

That was all she had wanted to hear, and more. Joy swept over her and left her weak, but still there was some uncertainty. She whispered, blinking back a film of tears the sudden overwhelming happiness had brought, "But—why didn't you tell me? Why—"

He shook his head. "You left so suddenly. I knew what it must have done to you"—there was deep sympathy in his eyes, a sharing of her pain—"and I knew you needed the time alone, but I wanted to be with you, to share it with you." And then a small, rueful smile touched his lips. "I almost ended up in jail again, you know. When your brother wouldn't tell me where you had gone, I tried to shake it out of him. Even then, all he could give me was a guess. It turns out it was a good one, fortunately," he added bitterly, "for him."

"But," she floundered, confused, "you didn't—"

"By then I had had time to think about it," he went on, his voice heavy with the memory of those first days. "Lindsey, it didn't occur to me that you might be thinking I blamed you. Believe me, if I had known, nothing would have kept me away. I thought you only needed the time to recover, and to get things in perspective...to pick up the pieces, as, if you recall," he added softly, "I told you you would someday." She nodded and dropped her eyes, remembering. Even then, he had known her better than she knew herself.

"So," he continued after a moment, "I did the next best thing. I sent my mother. Oh, not directly, of course, but I told her where you were, and I knew it would be only a matter of time before she could no longer resist the impulse to interfere in my life just once. Lindsey, please understand. There was nothing I could say to you, nothing I could offer you or promise you until after the election, and I knew my mother could deliver the only message that really mattered—that I still loved you."

She looked up at him, her eyes brimming with emotions too overpowering to be accepted, too tenuous to be believed in. She said, "I'm so glad you won."

"I am too. Until this moment, I didn't realize how glad." He brought his hands up to her shoulders hesitantly, as though afraid she might draw away or disappear before his eyes. His fingers closed lightly about her upper arms, and the deep light of sincerity appeared in his eyes. "This is my chance to make a difference, to change things for the better. I may not be the best man to ever hold the position, but it won't be for lack of trying."

She dropped her eyes briefly, and an unsteady sigh escaped her. "You can't change the world, Trey," she said sadly.

"No," he agreed, very soberly. "But I can change my corner of it . . . with you by my side."

Slowly he drew her into his arms, the tears spilled over as she wrapped her arms about his neck, and the dark day was suddenly awash with silver as her lips met his. Happiness so complete it transcended all else washed through her as at last she was able to commit fully to the only thing that had ever really mattered. She had been right in thinking that nothing would ever be the same between them, but it would be better, not worse. They had come through fire together, and nothing would ever threaten their love again.

"Oh, Lindsey," he whispered against her cheek at last, "will you come with me?"

She knew she had waited all her life to hear that question, and her joyous answer shown in her eyes. "Anywhere," she answered, and once again their lips met in a deep, unending kiss.

As they were locked in one another's embrace, it began to rain. It was just a sprinkle at first, then it grew harder, and then it was a cold, drenching downpour. Trey stepped back from her, rain pelting his shoulders and his hair and forming rivulets on his face, and laughter was dancing madly in his eyes.

"The most incredible things happen when I'm around you," he said.

He slipped his arm about her waist to urge her toward shelter, but she stopped, turning to him with happiness sparkling in her eyes and drops of rain quivering like tears on her lashes and her cheeks. She slipped her arms around him and simply held him, long and hard, one last time, before taking that first step of their new life together—a life filled with joy, adventure, and the magic of love.

Chapter Twelve

The door of Lindsey's elegant Bethesda home slammed resoundingly behind her as she burst into the foyer, flying across the gleaming parquet in barely two strides and rushing for the stairs.

The housekeeper hurried to catch her, calling, "Oh, Mrs. Sinclair, I'm glad you're home! The caterers—"

But Lindsey was late, and she had no time to deal with domestic affairs. She took the stairs two at a time and called back, "Do whatever you think best, Mrs. Withers. The flowers look great, by the way!"

"But Mrs. Sinclair—"

"I can't stop now, Mrs. Withers!" She paused at the top of the stairs to catch her breath and leaned over the railing, her tousled hair framing a somewhat impish face as she looked down at the distraught housekeeper. "If I don't hurry, I'm going to miss my own party. Is my husband home yet?"

"No—"

"Good!"

She hurried to her bedroom and closed the door on the housekeeper's indignant protests. She just had time for a bath as it was, for the first of the guests were due to arrive in less than half an hour, and she did not want Trey to see her looking so flustered and disorganized—

tonight of all nights. She allowed herself just a moment to sigh with regret as she sank down on the bed and kicked off her shoes, unzipping her dress in the same motion. She had so wanted a few moments alone with Trey tonight, before the party began. She scrunched her stockinged toes up in the white pile carpet and looked for a moment about the room she shared with Trey in utter contentment. It was large and elegant, with sky-blue wainscoting meeting carved white paneling, every third panel decorated with an airy white-and-blue fabric which matched the draperies. The furniture was Louis XIV, with an occasional mismatched piece she had chosen herself, and the entire effect was drawn together by an enormous vase of blue-and-white carnations on the table before the window which were brought in fresh daily. Lindsey had decorated this room herself, and Trey loved it, making her promise that when they returned to Atlanta their bedroom at home would be fashioned in exactly the same way.

Even before they were married, Trey had told her he intended to serve no more than one term of office. He had a definite timetable of goals he wished to accomplish while they were here, and beyond that politics held no more interest for him. So far, he was sticking to that timetable strictly and making amazing progress, so much so that, if his career in Washington continued on the course it had taken this past year, it was highly unlikely that his constituents would let him retire without a fight at the end of his term. Lindsey smiled happily as she remembered the highly complimentary article which had come out about him in a national magazine only today, one more thing they had to celebrate tonight....

Wearily, she pushed her way off the bed and padded to the adjoining bath, shedding garments as she went.

Trey would be home any minute, and if she hurried, there might be a few moments of privacy, after all....

While the bathroom filled with the steamy fragrance of scented bubbles she pinned her hair up and dumped her few pieces of jewelry on the vanity, experiencing a pang of sorrow as she looked at her bare ring finger. Trey had chided her so often about her absentminded habit of leaving her wedding ring on the vanity that pure horror had seized her and momentarily blocked out her grief when, three days ago, she had gone to slip it back on her finger and discovered it was missing. She had searched every corner, had Mrs. Withers turn the entire house upside down, and even called a plumber to dismantle the drains, but finally, with real tears in her eyes and trepidation in her voice, she had been forced to go to Trey and confess that she had lost the token of permanence he had so lovingly placed on her finger a year ago today.

He had taken it in stride, merely commenting mildly, "It was inevitable, wasn't it?" And then, seeing how upset she was, he assured her quickly, "We'll get you another. This time," he tried to tease her out of her misery, "with a padlock and chain that fastens around your wrist so you can't possibly lose it."

She sighed again as she sank into the warm bubbles up to her chin, stretching out her bare left hand and staring at it morosely. She supposed Trey couldn't be faulted for taking it so lightly; men just were not as sentimental as women. Lindsey was not superstitious, but nothing would ever replace that wide gold embossed band Trey had placed on her finger at the moment of their vows, and if she had it all to live over again she would have never, ever taken it off. She released an impatient breath and sank deeper into the water. One would think that a year of living in Washington, managing Trey's hectic office and whirlwind social schedule would have rid her of some of her most obvious absentminded traits. . . .

She had spent three days at Thanksgiving with her father. She had missed her flight, lost her luggage, and broken the heel on her shoe all before setting foot on the South Carolina coast, and her father's first enthusiastic greeting to her had been, "Washington hasn't changed you a bit!" She had laughingly retorted that, on the contrary, it was Trey who had changed, forgetting his briefcase, getting grocery lists interspersed with notes for his speeches, taking the wrong set of car keys, and with general good humor letting life with Lindsey have its inevitable effect on him. Trey was relaxed and perfectly at home in Washington, just as Lindsey herself was perfectly at home in any environment. The most important attribute he had acquired from her—or perhaps they had acquired it from each other—was the ability to take nothing too seriously, to recognize a dream in the midst of a nightmare, and to calmly and patiently hold on to a goal or an ideal when turmoil threatened to engulf it.

During the first month of their marriage, before the upheaval of the move to Washington, Trey had been Lindsey's strength. Disillusionment had opened her eyes to wisdom, but Trey had opened her eyes to the future. He had dispelled cynicism before it had time to take root, erased suspicion by showing her how easy it was to trust in him and his love, and taught her, gently and in stages, how to relax once again into the girl he had first loved. Lindsey had come to Washington wiser and stronger, but making up in love what she had lost in innocence.

Since then, they had been one another's strength, whether it was in drafting a speech, sitting up until the early hours of the morning discussing a legislative problem until it was solved, or rolling on the bed in peals of laughter like children over some potentially embarrassing incident which had occurred at one of the absurdly stuffy social functions which they were forced to attend.

"It's all a matter of perspective," Trey had told her once when, during their first few months of residence, Lindsey had begun to fear that everyone had been right after all—she simply would not fit in in Washington. "It's not where you are that counts, but who you're with."

So simple, but so true.

She sat up straight as she heard the door to the bedroom close and Trey's voice call exuberantly, "Good evening, Mrs. Senator, your hero has arrived! Where are the cheering crowds, the military band, the laurels?"

She wrapped herself quickly in a bath sheet and skipped into the bedroom, laughing. She paused before him, her color high with the warmth of the bath and with excitement, dripping steamy water onto the carpet, and she inquired demurely, "Do I kiss your ring, or will a simple curtsy do?"

He had already discarded his coat and tie, and was in the process of stripping off his shirt as he turned to her. His eyes raked her approvingly up and down, and he responded with a twinkle, "Curtsy, by all means. Let's see how well that towel holds up."

She ran to him and flung her arms about his neck, hugging him hard. "Congratulations to the star on the ascendant, the fastest rising young politician on the scene today, the young senator who is destined to leave his mark on Capitol Hill..."

She was quoting from the magazine article, and his

eyes reflected his own pleasure and unabashed pride as he looked down at her. "You read it?"

She laughed, stepping back a little and looping her wet arms about his neck. "Are you kidding? Everyone in Washington has read it by now. You want laurels— wait fifteen minutes till our guests arrive. We'll have to call in an industrial cleaning crew to sweep up all the laurels that are going to be thrown at you tonight!"

His eyes danced with happiness. "Not bad, for having been in office less than a year, huh?" And then he sobered. "But never let it be said I don't give credit where credit is due. I never would have made it without you, Lindsey, you know that, don't you?"

She nodded, shyly and happily, and he bent to kiss her lips once, lingeringly. Then, as though that taste were not enough, he pressed her damp body closer and took her lips again with gradually rising intensity, and eventually his hands found their way to the fastening of the towel at her breasts.

"How long do we have?" he murmured against her neck.

Although it was the last thing in the world she wanted to do, she pressed her hands to his chest and pushed him away. "Not long enough," she told him, with less firmness than she would have liked. "Get dressed."

"I have a better idea." He made to reach for her but she quickly sidestepped him. "All right," he sighed with a mock air of martyrdom. "This is no way to run a marriage, Lindsey."

She laughed, and he tossed his shirt onto the bed as she started toward the bathroom, insisting, "Come talk to me while I shower. It may be the last time I get to see you this evening."

"I have to get dressed!" she protested, but she knew

he was right. Too many of their moments alone were snatched while one or the other of them was in the shower, while he was shaving or she was dressing.... No way to run a marriage, indeed. *Why,* she thought in sudden irritation, *the baby will be in college before I get a chance to tell Trey he's going to be a father!* But then she smiled secretly to herself as she scooped up her underclothes and followed him into the bathroom to dress while he showered and told her about his day. There was so much to celebrate, and tonight, somehow, they were going to make room for them all.

"Did I tell you that I think I've got Senator Resnick swung over to our side on bill four-thirty-six?" he was saying as he turned off the water and she handed him a towel. "And where Resnick leads, three more are sure to follow. And, honey, will you make sure to cancel my lunch appointment on Thursday first thing in the morning? I've got to meet with the Canadian ambassador—"

"Write me a note!" she called over her shoulder as she went back into the bedroom, pulling out the brown chiffon dress she intended to wear tonight.

His voice receded as he moved into his dressing room. "How can I remember to write you a note," he complained, "if I only just this minute remembered to tell you about it?"

Lindsey quickly scribbled herself a note, and then reached into the drawer of her dressing table to take out a small, silver-wrapped package. Trey was just buttoning his dress trousers as she came into the dressing room, and his eyes, registering some surprise, noticed the package she held.

"What's this?" he demanded.

"Happy anniversary, Senator," she smiled, and pressed it into his hand.

He took it from her slowly. There was no mistaking the stunned surprise on his face as he finally looked up at her, nor the abject misery which crept into his eyes. "Oh, Lindsey," he began hesitantly. "Oh, God, honey, I'm sorry—I forgot!"

She fell back in absolute astonishment, staring at him.

He went on quickly, searching her eyes for a hint of forgiveness as swift emotions of confusion, apology, and rapid understanding swept his features. "That's what this party was all about tonight—why you insisted on having it on the tenth.... It never once crossed my mind, honey, I just didn't make the connection! What can I say? Are you very mad?"

She just couldn't believe it, and despite a small sense of hurt, she could not fight back a growing amusement. She, Lindsey, perpetual scatterbrain, had remembered, while he had forgotten! No one would have believed it if she were to tell them, and she intended to do just that. After all she had taken from him about her carelessness and forgetfulness, she was going to take enormous pleasure in holding this over his head the rest of his life. Besides, he looked so miserable and apologetic it was impossible to really be angry at him.

"Do you forgive me?" he pleaded.

She repressed a smile. "I'm not sure," she hedged.

He sighed, looking down at the elegantly wrapped gift in his hand. "I can't say that I blame you. I feel like a cad."

"You should," she assured him.

"After all," he said heavily, and the way he avoided her eyes made her immediately suspicious, "what could be worse than a husband forgetting his first wedding anniversary? It's almost as bad," he added, still not looking at her, "as a wife losing her wedding ring."

She stiffened in sharp perception, but when she

managed to catch a glimpse of his eyes there was nothing but bland regret there. She decided wisely to remain silent on that subject and insisted instead, somewhat grudgingly, "You may as well open your present."

He carefully unwrapped the package to discover, nestled in the tissue paper, a hand-painted miniature camel. She had searched for weeks to find one that he did not already have, and her efforts were rewarded by the look on his face as he drew it out.

"Do you like it?" she asked, but his obvious pleasure in the gift had already assured her of that, and was enough to wipe away any lingering resentment she might have had over his thoughtlessness.

He said, pressing the miniature into her hand, "Hold this for a minute."

"What—" she exclaimed as he swept her off her feet and into his arms. "What are you doing?"

"I am going," he told her firmly as he made his way into the bedroom, "to make love to my wife on our wedding anniversary." He deposited her firmly on the bed. "Any objections?"

"Yes!" she cried, though her rising color and the excitement in her eyes belied the statement. "We don't have time, we have to—"

He silenced her firmly with a kiss, resting his weight for a moment on his arms on either side of her. "We have all the time in the world."

"Trey—"

"Hush." He sat up for a moment, his face very serious, and took the miniature from her and set it carefully on the table by the bed. "Close your eyes," he commanded.

"What—"

His hand rested lightly across her eyes. "No peeking," he warned.

She giggled as she felt his weight lift from the bed, but she kept her eyes closed. "Isn't it a little late for modesty?" she teased. "Besides, Trey, really, what will our guests think? We can't—"

The mattress sagged again as he sat beside her, and she felt something small and square pressed into her hand. She opened her eyes hesitantly, and he was smiling gently down at her.

"You little dope," he said softly. "Did you really think I would forget?"

She sat up, wonder filling her eyes as she looked at the velvet box in her hand. "Oh, Trey," she whispered.

"I was going to punish you a little longer, you know," he went on casually as she fumbled to open it. "At least through dinner. But," he informed her and reached to open the spring catch of the box for her, "I found myself growing impatient for dessert."

Inside, gleaming richly against the dark-blue velvet, was her wedding ring. Tears of happiness and surprise stung her eyes and she could not speak.

"I took it to have it engraved," he confessed. "Read the inscription."

With trembling fingers, she lifted it from the box and turned the ring to the light. It was inscribed inside, "To have and to hold."

"And I mean that literally," he told her firmly, taking the ring from her. "Don't ever take it off again."

He slipped it on her finger, and she whispered tremulously, "I won't! Oh, I won't!" And she threw her arms about his neck, kissing him violently.

"And now," he murmured against her mouth much later, "let's start acting like a married couple, shall we?"

The intensity of the kiss had left her lying weakly

back against the pillows, and she barely retained the presence of mind to whisper, "Our guests—"

"If they have any sense," he interrupted her huskily, slipping the straps of her coffee-colored slip off her shoulders, "are at home right now, doing exactly what we're doing."

A small measure of confusion penetrated the tingling, soporific pleasure his touch was generating. "W-what?"

He sighed impatiently, pressing one warm kiss into the hollow of her throat before straightening up again. "Do you remember those invitations you asked me to mail?" he reminded her, and she nodded. "I conveniently forgot to do it. I also called the caterers and changed the dinner for twelve to a dinner for two—"

"*That*'s what Mrs. Withers was trying to tell me this afternoon!" she exclaimed.

"Well, I couldn't tell her," he admitted. "She would have blown the whole surprise."

She laughed happily, wrapping her arms about his neck. "You and your surprises!"

He smiled indulgently. "Now can we stop talking, Mrs. Sinclair?"

She sighed, "Yes," and drew him into her arms.

"TREY," she whispered into the darkness a long time later, shifting her head on his shoulder to try to get a look at his face. "Are you asleep?"

"No," he answered, his hand caressing her shoulder. "Just starving."

She smiled to herself and looked at the darkened ceiling, catching his hand at her shoulder. "Before we eat...there's something I've been meaning to tell you."

"Oh-oh." He rested his forearm across his brow with

a heavy sigh of resignation. "That tone of voice usually precedes a confession. What have you forgotten this time?"

She giggled. She couldn't help it, when he put it like that, it sounded so funny.... "Well, as a matter of fact," she replied, "do you remember that party for the Egyptian ambassador a couple of months ago? We had such a good time and we got home so late..."

"And you got a little tipsy," he remembered.

"I did not," she objected immediately, and then admitted reluctantly, "Well, maybe a little."

"So what did you do?" he insisted, turning to look at her. "Leave your purse? Forget your fur?"

She shook her head, delighting in teasing him. "It was nothing I did at the party.... More like what we did when we got home."

He thought for a moment, but no more than that. His soft intake of breath signaled his remembrance, but he said nothing. She supplied, just in case he had not already reached the logical conclusion, "I'm pregnant."

He said nothing.

"Trey?" She sat up, bending over him, but his face was unreadable in the darkness. And still he said nothing.

She was becoming alarmed. They had planned on a family, but those plans had always been somewhere in the distant future, for Trey had said many times that Washington was no place to raise a child. She knew Trey wanted children as much as she did, but—as usual—her timing left much to be desired. She felt a sinking feeling begin in her stomach as she suspected he was not as happy with the news as she was, but she managed somewhat tremulously, "Trey? Are you—are you upset?"

Slowly, and with cascading relief, she heard the first sounds of his soft, repressed laughter reach her. Yet as much as she was relieved, she was indignant and confused, and she demanded, "What's so funny?"

"It's just," he exclaimed softly, shaking with suppressed chuckles, "that I was beginning to think there was nothing you could do to surprise me!" He reached for her, and his eyes glinted in the dark. "Although why it should surprise me, I don't know. You always were accident-prone."

But she hesitated, poised above him as his fingers tightened on her shoulders. "Are—are you sure—you don't mind? Are you happy, I mean?"

He laughed again, and now there was no mistaking the pure pleasure in his voice. "Happy? Give me one reason why I shouldn't be the happiest man in the world! I'll show you happy." His arms tightened about her. "Come here," he commanded throatily.

She came, gladly.

HARLEQUIN *Love Affair*

This month's titles

A MATTER OF TRUST *Rebecca Flanders*

Lindsey Madison forgets little things like housekeys, pocket money, and to lock her front door at night. When she comes from Iowa to Atlanta to help her uncle in his campaign for a Senate seat, she intends to focus all of her energy on his re-election. Trey Sinclair, often called Washington's most eligible bachelor, wants to be the new senator from Georgia. He has committed himself to the pressures and obligations of a long, hard campaign and a successful term of office. Lindsey and Trey—on opposite sides of a political battle until their undeniable love joins them as one!

THE SAME LAST NAME *Kathleen Gilles Seidel*

April Peters knew that Christopher Ramsey did not love her when they married. But Christopher's genteel Virginian background dictated that a woman about to have your baby became your wife in a hurry . . . Innocently April believed that Christopher would grow to love her once they were a family, until her baby died at birth and she was propelled into cold, harsh reality. She left Christopher without a trace as to her whereabouts. Six years later as a successful State Forest Ranger April meets Christopher again. In the serene setting of a natural preserve, old passions turn to mature desires too powerful to be controlled!

CITY LIFE, CITY LOVE *Beverly Sommers*

Raising a child alone in Manhattan wasn't easy for Betsy Miller. But after her divorce she wanted to start afresh. Her night-time job as a secretary in a law office gave Betsy the freedom she longed for. Betsy's life-style was finally her own, until she made a costly error one night at work—and met Nick Creme. As the firm's hottest lawyer, Nick posed the kind of obstacle Betsy could not ignore. And Nick surely demanded all of Betsy's attention. . . .

UNTAMED HEART *Elda Minger*

Lions and tigers were a part of Samantha Collins's life-style. As a trainer living in Hollywood, Samantha was used to working with exotic animals in lush locales. Her love for large cats and wild beasts brings her to Puerto Rico, when she gets word about a troublesome tiger on a film set. She flies to join the crew immediately—despite the rumours about the skirt-chasing reputation of the movie director, Ryan Fitzgerald. Samantha never expected to have to tame Ryan's savage soul . . .

NOW AND FOREVER   *Sharon McCaffree*

When Jeannie Rasmussen met Paul Raymond for the first time, she knew that he was something special. But as a highly self-sufficient woman, Jeannie had sheltered herself from relationships since becoming a widow twelve years earlier. Jeannie had her son to raise, and did not want to lean on anyone else's resources for support. Paul felt the attraction, too. He knew that with his own two children, Jeannie would think he was only interested in having her around as a surrogate mother. The warmth of two families and the experience of parenting bring Jeannie and Paul together, but the sparks that ignite into flames of passion in the hot Arizona desert bond them as one!

TWICE IN A LIFETIME   *Rebecca Flanders*

Barbara Ellis didn't think so, at least not until she met Kyle Waters. Tall and ruggedly handsome, Kyle's piercing green eyes told Barbara that he was a man who got what he wanted at any cost—both in his work as an architect and in his personal life. She still treasured her dead husband's memory, and did not want to be unfaithful to the only man she had ever loved. At least not until Kyle began to stir an unbridled passion deep within her, one that he met with a fiery desire of his own!

LOVE CHANGES   *Barbara Bretton*

It took Stacey Andersen five years to put the pieces of her life back together after her fiancé walked out. As a successful businesswoman with part ownership in a small computer company, Stacey was satisfied—until Franco Borelli exploded into her peaceful world. Sophisticated and secure, Franco shook her very core, and with burning ecstasy threatened the deepest, darkest secret any woman could ever reveal!

HOSTAGE HEART   *Renee Roszel*

Drew McKenna was on the run. With the threat of her ex-husband returning to their hometown, Drew was glad to have an excuse to flee to Germany to visit with old friends. When she left Los Alamos, New Mexico, however, she never thought that she would almost lose the most precious gift shared by all Americans—her U.S. citizenship. Rolf Erhardt wanted to escape. He didn't care about anything except freedom. When fate brought Drew to his life, Rolf saw his ticket out. Neither Drew nor Rolf realized that their need to be free from past bonds could never match their burning desire for one another!

To be published in February,
four more absorbing novels
from

HARLEQUIN
SuperRomance

DANCE-AWAY LOVER by Casey Douglas
Since the tragic accident that had all but ended her
career in ballet, Raine had feared she would never
dance again. Could the challenge from the merciless
choreographer, Brandon du Rivage, erase that fear?

DARK SIDE OF LOVE by Peggy Bechko
In claiming her inheritance — a sprawling ranch in a
remote part of Mexico—Sirena knew she had
accepted a challenge. But she was unprepared for
the antagonism of her adviser, the dark, aristocratic
Ramón Savedel.

LOVE'S SOUND IN SILENCE by Meg Hudson
Midge found herself more than a little intrigued by
the handsome young newspaper publisher, Brian
Vandervelt, and she impulsively committed herself
to a three-month copywriting job on his paper. But
it seemed there was no scaling the private wall Brian
had built around himself.

SWEET TEMPTATION by Shannon Clare
Liza respected the power Christian Chase radiated
in the art world, but how dare he suggest that her
fiancé's religious cross was a fake! Somehow Liza
had to verify its authenticity, even though it meant
travelling to the Middle East—and there she had
little chance to escape from Christian's passionate
pursuit of her . . .